Bellevue Literary Review

*A journal of humanity
and human experience*

Including:

*Plagues and Pens:
Writers Examine Infectious Diseases*

Volume 5, Number 2, Fall 2005
Department of Medicine
New York University School of Medicine
www.BLReview.org

The *Bellevue Literary Review* is published twice a year by the Department of Medicine at New York University School of Medicine.

Subscriptions available at www.BLReview.org (1 year: $12 ♦ 3 years: $30)

The Editors invite submissions of previously unpublished works of fiction, nonfiction, and poetry that touch upon relationships to the human body, illness, health, and healing. We encourage creative interpretation of these themes. Manuscripts can be submitted at www.BLReview.org.

© 2005 Department of Medicine, New York University School of Medicine
550 First Avenue, OBV-612, New York, NY 10016
Printed by The Sheridan Press   Hanover, Pennsylvania
Distributed by Ingram Periodicals and Bernhard DeBoer, Inc.
ISSN 1537-5048   ISBN 0-9727573-5-X
Indexed by the American Humanities Index

The Editorial Staff of the *Bellevue Literary Review* express their deep appreciation to the following people who have assisted with editorial review: Sonya Abrams, Sarah Bain, David Baldwin, Robin Black, Denitza Blagev, Toby Bochan, Andrew Bomback, Carlos Caprioli, Ana Chavier, Marcia Day Childress, Manesh Dagli, Rebecca Dillingham, Judith Dunford, Kay Elliott, Steven Field, Madina Gerasimov, Will Grossman, Meghan Hickey, Marie Holmes, David Hong, Judy Katz, Jackie Keer, April Krassner, Florence Kugel, Suzanne McConnell, Michelle McMacken, Jacqueline Mosher, Elayne Mustalish, Danielle Newman, Ruth Oratz, Marco Rafala, Pamela Rosenthal, Benjamin Sadock, Peter Selgin, Shetal Shah, Jana Unkel, Benj Vardigan, Lisa Voltolina, Julia Weis, Carol Zoref.

We thank Benjamin Akman for upgrading the BLR online submission program with the support of the Council of Literary Magazines and Presses (CLMP) and the NYU Department of Medicine. We also acknowledge the School of Medicine IT Department for developing and maintaining this program. We are grateful for the help of Lorinda Klein, and for the continued support of Bellevue Hospital.

Cover Note: Photo taken in the garden of Bellevue Hospital, circa 1955. This child most likely had polio. On June 27, 1927, Bellevue Hospital was the recipient of the first iron lung ever used for the treatment of paralytic poliomyelitis. (June 27th is sometimes commemorated as "Iron Lung Day.") Iron lungs were still in use at Bellevue until well into the 1970s. During the peak years of polio, in the 1930s and 1940s, patients were usually transferred to the Willard Parker Hospital for Infectious Diseases on the Lower East Side. The use of iron lungs decreased once the polio vaccines of Jonas Salk and Albert Sabin became available. Both Salk and Sabin received their medical training at NYU and did most of their medical rotations at Bellevue. Salk's injectable "killed" vaccine was introduced and licensed in 1955. This was the first effective vaccine to prevent the paralytic complications of polio. Sabin's 1961 oral "live" vaccine led to further reductions in spread of the disease. Together, these vaccines have eliminated naturally occurring polio from the Western Hemisphere and from nearly the entire world.

Bellevue Literary Review

A journal of humanity and human experience

Contents

Volume 5, Number 2, Fall 2005

Plagues and Pens:
Writers Examine Infectious Diseases

Nonfiction

Fiction

Poetry

Foreword

The Fall 2005 issue of the *Bellevue Literary Review* contains a special focus on writings about infectious diseases. This seems particularly appropriate, since Dr. Martin Blaser, the publisher of the *BLR*, is slated to become President of the Infectious Diseases Society of America this year.

Evan Lyon's essay *The Only Fat Man in Lascahobas* interweaves the opulent life of a local funeral director in Haiti with vodou rituals and the death of Saintilus Joseph, a poor man with tuberculosis and AIDS. In the poem *The Porch*, Katherine Soniat speaks of the Saranac Tuberculosis Sanitorium. "The wilderness cure, it was called/ as countless inhaled, then petitioned the cold/ to polish each lung clean." AIDS, in "*Silence=Death*" by Rafael Campo, is symbolized by a "worn-out T-shirt, black as mourning, black/ as countless deaths."

Influenza, the great pandemic of 1918, is vividly depicted in Marcia Calhoun Forecki's story, *The Gift of the Spanish Lady,* when she writes, "The news of a death was often the first word of a victim's illness," and in Priscilla Atkins' poem, *The Sky Gone White*, which reminds us that "In 1918, thousands more/ than died in the trenches/ died of the flu."

The deadly bubonic plague is recalled in William Orem's *Plague Year*. "I remember Pastor saying/ there was something not quite/ safe in how the sun was setting...Then he went/ as well." The plague is still present today, carried by "delightful-looking rodents called marmots," as described in the essay *Quarantine* by Matt Davis, a Peace Corps worker in Mongolia.

Hansen's disease is seen through the eyes of Gar, a government worker, whose job it was to transport a sensitive young woman to the leprosy hospital in Pat Tompkins' story, *The Road to Carville*. In the poem, *Mary Sees Her Daughter*, Eve Rifkah describes how Mary Martin, a young woman from the Cape Verde Islands, is also taken to Carville. "Mary is placed in a wheelbarrow/ trundled to the train/ face shawled and shrouded/ shoulders shake in rage and sorrow/ Mary don't you weep don't you mourn."

In addition to the selections that focus on infectious disease, this issue features other writings on our general theme of illness and healing. We are delighted to welcome back Bob Oldshue and Cortney Davis, as they each make their third appearance in the *BLR*. We hope you enjoy our attention to *Plagues and Pens*, as well as the broader landscape of the *BLR*.

Jerome Lowenstein, MD
Nonfiction Editor

Plagues & Pens:
Writers Examine Infectious Diseases

Special section of the *Bellevue Literary Review*
Volume 5, Number 2, Fall 2005

Publishers Note: We are pleased to bring out this new feature of the *Bellevue Literary Review*—themed sections. A concentration on infectious diseases always is fitting for a journal of the medical humanities, and as HIV and other menaces stalk the globe, it is topical. The volume of relevant material we received was substantial; only a small fraction could be published.

We are grateful to the Lucius N. Littauer Foundation for its support of this special project.

We hope to have other themed issues in the future.

Martin J. Blaser, MD
Publisher

The Road to Carville

Pat Tompkins

The back of his shirt was stuck to the car seat, and it wasn't noon yet. When the road plowed through forest, Garlan Hamilton slowed during the stretches of shade. A ball game crackled on the radio. "Strike," said Gar, trying to predict the next pitch. But it was ball three. "Aw, he's gonna walk him." He favored the Sox because he'd seen them in Chicago once during the war. A fine city. But maybe he wouldn't enjoy Chicago now. He hadn't liked much since the Army.

Gar didn't particularly like his job—"Hell, that's why they call it work," he'd say—but he didn't hate it the way some people did. His job had some pluses. He traveled some, at government expense, and nobody bothered him. He listened to whatever he wanted on the radio as he guided the four-door DeSoto down dirt roads, trailing rust-colored clouds. He wanted to be left alone.

Gar rarely passed another car, and the few houses he saw were little better than tin-roof shacks. He was thinking about lunch when he saw the dead armadillo on the side of the road. Poor guy. They came out at night and had bad eyesight. To fend off predators, they could roll into a ball, but such tactics would not save them from barreling trucks. Gar sympathized with the odd-looking creatures. In his teens, during the Depression, his family had eaten armadillo for dinner a couple times a month. His father called them "Hoover hogs." They did taste like lean pork, but without their shell, they looked defenseless, more possum than pig. Gar had since learned that people could get leprosy from eating armadillo meat. Had his parents known that? You could get sick from undercooked pork, too; it just wasn't something you thought about when you were hungry.

During the third inning, he stopped for gas. Gar plucked a Coca-Cola from watery ice in a red metal locker, handed a nickel to a teenage boy, and flipped off the cap. "Yes, sir," he said after he drained half the bottle. He held the Coke against his neck, while plucking at his damp shirt with his free hand. "How far's it to Youngerton?" he asked the boy.

"Twelve miles."

Maybe it was a lingering thought of bad meat, but Gar decided not to stop at the barbecue stand he'd had in mind earlier. He bought a bag of shelled peanuts instead and chewed them as he drove, one elbow on the windowsill. A heron in a patch of swamp near the road lifted a twiglike leg and tested the water with its foot. A thick canopy of branches—sweetgum, box elder, tupelo—filtered the heat of the sun. Yes, this surely beat his last job working at the post office: two years fiddling around with stamps and small change in a dim, stuffy room. But even that job had a plus: you never took it home in your head. You might be numb from the routine, but you didn't worry about the mail that passed through your hands. Delivering the post as a mailman would have been ideal, but all that walking would have killed his feet, his left foot anyway.

At a massive oak bearded with gray moss, the road forked. A wooden sign shaped like an arrow pointed left: Youngerton. The one facing right said Rocheau. Gar considered going right, as he did at some point on every trip lately—just keep driving and never return. But he dutifully headed left and when he reached the outskirts of the town, he gripped the wheel with both hands and stopped whistling. He began looking for the McPhersons' house, 161 Cypress.

This was the hard part. No one was ever glad to see him arrive. Gar stumbled getting out of the car, partly from sitting so long, partly because of his bad foot. He stumbled more lately, it seemed, or maybe he just noticed it more. He'd lost three toes during the war. No heroic action, though. Some idiot dogface had run over his left foot with a forklift two weeks before V-E Day. The damage—a hangnail compared to injuries he'd seen—left a dull, constant ache. On the McPhersons' doorstep, he passed his hands over his wavy brown hair, then wiped his palms on his pants before ringing the bell.

A stout woman wearing an apron over her dress opened the door and stood behind the screen door. "Yes?" she whispered. He detected the fear in her one word.

"Afternoon, ma'am. I'm from the government, here to pick up your daughter." Through the dark screen, he saw her eyes shine with tears.

"Yes," she whispered again and pushed the screen door open so he could step inside.

Gar had seen many cases, so he was prepared not to flinch when he met this girl. Yet he had to check himself from reacting as the mother led her daughter forward. Eldonna was 15, with copper-colored hair and the greenest eyes he'd ever seen. Her skin was clear aside from a sprinkle of freckles.

More than 20 years before the war, the federal government had taken over Carville Hospital from the state of Louisiana. The only hospital in the country for leprosy patients was now officially named the Hansen Center, but everyone still called it Carville. If a boy in Shreveport got in trouble, his mother might say, "I'm going to send you to Carville if you don't behave."

No one who went to Carville ever left. Most of the patients Gar took to Carville lacked obvious signs of the disease. The horrible parts came later: amputations, blindness, disfigurement. He'd seen that mainly in photos, but it was enough for him.

Last week, Gar had collected another person newly diagnosed with leprosy, a 26-year-old farmer with a wife and two kids. The man's suitcase was packed, but when the time came to leave, he refused to go. Gar had to handcuff him and force him into the back of the station wagon. He'd used his handcuffs only once before. Usually he never had to touch the people he drove to Carville, although he'd convinced himself that he was unlikely to pick up the disease from them. The doctors who diagnosed them didn't catch it; the nuns who staffed the hospital in Carville stayed clean; a husband could have it and his wife would be healthy, like the couple last week. Most of his passengers were numb with dismay, numb like the patches of skin on their ear lobes or knees that first indicated something was wrong. They stared out the car window, memorizing the landscape.

It was a shame anyone had to go to Carville, a pity there was no cure, but Gar had been to war and knew how little fairness had to do with anything. Still, when he looked at Eldonna McPherson, he wanted to punch someone. Like the doctor who'd condemned her. Gar's job was part of the Public Health Service, but nobody thanked him for what he was doing. The farm woman last week had said, "What do they pay y'all to come steal my husband? You're no better than a bounty hunter."

"I'll take your grip," Gar said and picked up the girl's suitcase. He held out his other hand toward the round hatbox she held, but the girl shook her head and stepped back. "I'll be out by the car when you're ready," he said.

He leaned against a willow tree and smoked a cigarette, a habit he'd picked up in the Army. Gar glanced at the pack. Lucky Strike. What sort of name was that? Lucky. Huh. He wondered about the hatbox. What would she need a good hat for in Carville? For chapel. For funerals. Gar wanted a glass of ice water and needed a toilet, but he did not want to return to the house and ask for favors. He stepped behind the tree instead.

Gar was about to light up again when he heard the screen door open. The mother and daughter walked hand in hand to the dusty station wagon. Their chins quivered and pointed to the ground. They embraced and the woman had to force herself to release the girl. She stepped back and stared at Gar. "Don't worry, ma'am," he said. "I'll get her there safe and sound by this evening."

"Call me when you get there," the mother said.

"I'll call you tomorrow." Eldonna turned toward Gar. "I can do that, can't I?"

"Sure. You can call anytime," he said, although he wasn't certain this was true. Gar opened the back door and Eldonna got in. After waving good-bye until she could no longer see her mother, she wrapped her arms around the hatbox on her lap.

A few miles passed in silence before Gar said, "Mind if I turn on the radio?"

"No, sir. I don't mind."

"Anything you want to listen to?"

"It doesn't matter to me."

He tuned in a station of popular music, love songs, music to dance to. Years ago, he'd been a fair dancer. That's how he'd met his girlfriends, at dances. It certainly wasn't his handsome face—with its bulbous nose and acne-scarred cheeks—that won him dancers. But on the dance floor, his stocky figure turned almost graceful, moving with the music. When Nat King Cole started crooning "Mona Lisa," Gar listened to a verse, then changed stations. He glanced occasionally at his passenger in the rear-view mirror. Eldonna was a helluva lot prettier than any Mona Lisa. Eldonna's mouth had full lips, closed, not smiling or frowning. She'd probably never really been kissed by a man. Chances were, she never would. Patients at Carville weren't allowed to date or marry; men and women didn't even eat together in the dining hall. Not that there weren't ways around the rules. But if a patient had a baby, she wasn't allowed to keep it. He looked again in the mirror, noticing her breasts, then was immediately ashamed of himself.

Maybe it was better to go in young and not know what you were missing. This girl would always sleep alone, with no one to stroke her long, shiny hair or her slender neck or her soft thighs or—Jesus, man, get a hold of yourself. She was a leper; that smooth skin would become scaly, with ulcers and sores. He shrugged his tense shoulders and searched the radio for another baseball game, then switched it off.

The woods gave way to high, bright fields of sugar cane. When he'd come home on leave, Gar had seen German prisoners of war in the fields, cutting cane. Hot work; it made your back sore and your arms ache. He'd been surprised, then glad to see that the damn jerries weren't sitting on their duffs. Shit, he thought now, the cane cutters had been on vacation compared to what they did to our POWs. Helluva way to treat people. Had Eldonna seen the Germans in the cane fields when she was younger? What could they talk about? The war probably wasn't a good subject.

Gar spotted a dark, furry lump in the center of the road and swerved to avoid it.

"Mister, would you stop the car? Please?"

He glanced in the mirror. Was she carsick? He pulled over on the gravel shoulder. "What's wrong?" He turned to face her, but she was peering out the rear windshield. In a flash she was out the door and hurrying down the road. She covered 50 yards before Gar shouted, "Hey." He trotted after her. He couldn't run worth a damn anymore. That girl could outrace him easy. Was she trying to escape, hide in the forest of sugar cane?

When he caught up with her, she was bent over gray fur, a raccoon. Eldonna held her hand close to its snout. "He's still alive."

Gar crouched down. Sure enough. No blood on the road. Good thing he'd swerved.

"Maybe he's just stunned." Eldonna moved to pick it up.

"Hold on now. You don't want to be handling that. It could be rabid."

He pulled Eldonna over to the shoulder although no other cars were in sight.

"We can't leave him there," she said.

"Let me check the car. I might have some gloves."

"I know what." Eldonna ran back to the car and removed a wide-brimmed yellow hat from its box. She brought the empty hatbox back to the raccoon before Gar had even reached the car. He returned flexing his fingers in thick canvas gloves. With his hands, he scooped up the warm body.

"Be careful," Eldonna said. He meant to move it to the side of the road, but she held out the box. "Put him in here."

The animal felt lopsided. "I think one of its rear legs is broke."

"The doctors at Carville can fix that." She took the box from him and studied the raccoon, wrapped in its bushy tail. "He looks scared."

Gar saw the restless button eyes and nodded. "Probably his first time in a lady's hatbox."

Her smile—the first time he'd seen it—pierced Gar. Had he been fully awake before?

He shook his head as they headed back to the car. "I don't think they'll be wanting you to bring a pet to Carville."

"I won't keep him. When he's better, I'll let him go." Eldonna embraced the box. "He must be thirsty."

"We'll stop at the next gas station and get some water."

"Thank you."

Gar wiped his face with his handkerchief before starting the car. How was this girl going to survive in Carville?

They stopped at a Mobil station near a crossroads. While a boy pumped gas, they discussed how to get the animal to drink. He should stay in the box but a bowl wouldn't fit in it. "We need a baby bottle," Eldonna said.

Gar explained the problem to the boy who was cleaning the windshield. "Anywhere around here we can get one?"

"How about an eye dropper?" the boy said. "My mom used that with a baby bunny she found last spring."

"That sounds fine. But do y'all have one?"

The boy, Alan Hargitty, offered to phone his mother. "We live nearby. You could stop and pick it up."

While he called, Gar fetched two Cokes. He and Eldonna drank the sodas as they stood in the shadow cast by the tall sign advertising the gas station, a large red winged horse on a white background. "My Uncle Jason has horses," she said. "He lets me ride them."

Gar nodded. He'd heard lots of things about Carville, but nothing about there being any horses. It wasn't a resort. Somehow the patients filled up their days. Or got through the days. Empty days. Empty years. He stared at the Mobil sign; he'd seen it at countless stations throughout the state. But he noticed the horse's wings as though for the first time. And he began to think that he would not drive Eldonna to Carville after all.

Alan gave them directions to his house. Gar shook his hand and slipped a dollar in his shirt pocket.

"Thank you so much," Eldonna said. She started to offer her hand and then stopped.

The boy looked puzzled but said, "Good luck."

On her front porch, Mrs. Hargitty showed Eldonna how to feed the raccoon. "Just give him a dropper or two at a time. He might be hurt inside." She gave them the glass dropper with its small bottle.

"Where y'all headed?" she asked.

"Baton Rouge," Gar said.

"That's a ways. I'll get some more water."

In the car, Eldonna finished feeding the raccoon. "Why'd you say Baton Rouge?"

"It's none of her business where we're going."

"She was very nice."

"Yes, she was." She wouldn't accept any money and had offered them lemonade. She might not have been so friendly if he'd said Carville. "Has that water perked up your patient?"

"I think so."

Baton Rouge wasn't far from Carville. What if he drove there—or somewhere else? He considered the possibilities, shimmering before him like the mirages on the parched roadway. They could go to New Orleans. He could leave her to the big city; New Orleans was full of lost souls and shadowy places. But what would a country girl do there except get taken advantage of? He didn't have enough money with him to get her settled in a boarding house. He could turn around and take her back to her mother and quit this job. That would get him off the hook, but not her. The government would send someone else to take Eldonna to Carville. Perhaps she had relatives somewhere who would help her.

"Have you always lived in Youngerton?" He stretched his arm across the top of the seat and glanced back at her.

"Yes, sir."

"Ever travel any? Visit relatives?"

"I went to Mardi Gras when I was ten. And we went to the state capitol building on a field trip last year." He found out that she had an aunt and cousins near Lake Charles whom she'd visited years ago, when a cousin married.

As though confirming something he already knew, Gar nodded. Damn. There wasn't going to be an easy solution. "Do you have brothers and sisters?" He looked at her in the rear-view mirror.

"Two sisters; one's married and one's younger than me. My brother died in the war. On Guam."

Gar nodded again. "I was in the Army. Volunteered. Sent to France." Now he was thinking about going AWOL. Did soldiers plan that or was it a sudden decision? Maybe you couldn't do it if you thought too much about it. Gar remembered that one of his Army buddies was from Baton Rouge. Andy Fontaine. Guys called him Ace because he could bluff his way through any poker hand. They hadn't kept in touch, but Andy was someone Gar felt he could rely on. Maybe Ace would have an idea. He could call him. Stop somewhere for dinner. Yes, he'd phone Andy.

The sun would not set for another hour at least, but the June heat was finally simmering down. Gar turned on the radio again. Patti Page zipping through some happy-go-lucky love song. Usually, he didn't do more than stop at gas stations with his passengers. He ate after delivering them to Carville. Turning down the music, Gar announced, "We'll stop for dinner soon." He glanced in the mirror; Eldonna was focused on the hatbox in her lap. He swatted at a butterfly that had blown into the car. Jesus, this heat. I'm not much hungry, he thought, but it'll give me a chance to call Andy.

"He needs something to eat, too," Eldonna said.

"Raccoons'll eat near anything." He remembered the bag of peanuts from the morning. Still in the glove box. "Here, try these." He passed the bag to the girl.

She poured a handful in the box; the raccoon only sniffed them. He pulled into a dirt lot alongside the Ice Box, which looked more like a juke joint than a cafe. "They sure know how to fix crawfish here," Gar said. Eldonna didn't move, so he opened the car door for her. "All the iced tea you can drink, too," he said, hoping to coax a grin from the girl.

Inside, the cafe was cool and dim, as though the shade of the oaks penetrated the roof. They sat in a booth and Gar told her to order whatever she wanted—"It's on the government," which was true only because it paid his salary. Then he excused himself to make a phone call. The phone was near the bar, around a corner from the cafe. It took several minutes for the operator to find Andy's number in Baton Rouge. Gar rehearsed what he would say. He had thought to tell the straight story; that would be easiest, but that idea seemed less easy as he imagined Andy's surprise at hearing from him.

Gar, you sonofagun. Where are you? What are you doing?

I'm driving a leper to Carville.

No, it sounded like a bad joke. How could he ask Andy what to do about Eldonna? The phone rang again and again, each brrinng sounding like a bleat for *Aaaaace*. After more than a dozen rings, he hung up. Gar passed a hand through his hair and stared at the dial as though he didn't recognize the letters and numbers.

Back at the booth was a pitcher of iced tea and two tall glasses, but no Eldonna. He glanced around the room; he didn't see her. His first thought was that she'd run away. Gar poured a glass of tea and stirred in sugar. It probably meant his job; you weren't supposed to lose lepers. What was a job anyway, except something you wouldn't do unless you were paid to? The glass wet against his palm, he gulped the iced tea, as strong and sweet as dark rum. Then he played with the long-handled spoon, turning it end over end. Run, Eldonna.

His eyes were closed when he heard the whoosh of the seat cushion as Eldonna sat down across from him. Gar dropped the spoon. "Where'd you go?"

"I had to use the ladies' room," she said and filled her glass with iced tea.

He nodded as if to say, I knew that. He almost said, "What's taking them so long?" but stopped himself. They were in no hurry, but he couldn't think of anything to say to the girl with the shiny copper hair. It hung in soft waves to her collarbones. She'd only taken a sip of the tea.

"Would you rather have a Coke?"

She shook her head. "This is fine, it's just too strong."

He asked the waitress for some lemon. "Thank you," Eldonna said as she picked up a wedge from the small bowl.

"Speak up if there's anything else you want."

She squeezed the lemon over the tea. A squirt of juice hit his nose.

"I'm sorry," she said.

"It's a big target." She smiled and he smiled back. "I like mint in my tea," he added.

"Me too. We've got a big patch of spearmint by the garage."

"I put in a whole sprig and then mash the leaves with my spoon." He stopped, abashed, as he noticed the waitress approaching. What was he doing, talking about fresh mint? At Carville, you were probably lucky to get ice in your iced tea.

They ate dinner without talking, surrounded by the buzz of others in the restaurant, their utensils clinking against plates and cups. He insisted she order dessert. "Never known a girl who didn't like dessert," he said.

While she dragged her spoon around the sherbet as though peeling an orange, Gar telephoned Andy again. Maybe they could stay with Andy a few days until he figured out how to rescue Eldonna. No answer. Sure, get charged with kidnapping. As he counted the rings, a band started playing in a corner of the bar. Several couples danced to a swing tune where tables and chairs had been cleared. What was he thinking? Andy wouldn't be home on a Friday night.

When Gar returned to the booth, he noticed that most of the sherbet had melted. The girl's fingers tapped on the tabletop. "Pretty good band," he said. Except for a booth with two men who resembled bullfrogs, Gar and Eldonna were the only customers still sitting. He thought of asking her to dance. He hadn't danced in years.

He lit a cigarette and closed his eyes, picturing himself and the girl dancing. Instead, Gene Kelly intruded in a scene from "On the Town." What a dancer. Did they show movies at Carville? Would lepers want to see a musical? Gar sighed and ground out the spark in the cigarette.

Eldonna's fingers weren't moving to the rhythm of the song.

"Nervous?" he asked.

"I guess." She stood up. "We'd better be going."

Outside, the crickets shrieked. On their way to the car, Gar thought of what he'd like to say. I'm sorry. I don't want to take you to Carville. It's my job, but I'm quitting. It's a lousy job. You're the last person I'm ever taking to Carville. Another voice said, And what good will that do her? You'll feel better and she'll still be in Carville.

He opened the back door for Eldonna and circled the car, once, then twice. He slapped the roof with his palm. "Damnation." Then Gar got behind the driver's wheel. "How's that raccoon?"

"He's asleep. But the peanuts are gone."

'That's a good sign."

Soon it would be dark, with the tall cypress and pines blocking the quarter moon. This stretch of road resembled a tunnel. A blaze of headlights would bring the only light, abrupt and bright. Armadillos would wander out, awkward and nearsighted. Their armor plating wouldn't protect them from a moving car. A sudden death. Maybe they were lucky that way. Garlan Hamilton drove to Carville for the final time. ❧

Mary Sees Her Daughter

Eve Rifkah

The tug, *John T. Sherman*, docks in New Bedford
thirteen hesitant—the last—crawl or carried from shaking boat
to land, eye the gathered masses, the train
readied for the long pull to Louisiana.

four grandchildren huddle on the outskirts
of the crowd
Mother, a woman calls
from twelve years of separation
the attendants hold her back
promise not to touch   not to embrace
daughter agrees
a brief visit   no hugs but pleas
and tears   mouths open in supplication
Mary whispers   *take me home*
I'm not sick   they tell me I'm sick
Mary unable to stand
in the arms of an attendant

the town folk look away
tears mist the curious eyes
Mary is placed in a wheelbarrow
trundled to the train
face shawled and shrouded
shoulders shake in rage and sorrow

Mary don't you weep don't you mourn

&

Mary Martin, 44, Cape Verdean, immigrated in 1902, arrived at Penikese Island Leper Hospital, December 17, 1909. She denied being a leper and gradually lost her mind. Mary was transferred to the new leprosarium in Carville, Louisiana, in 1921, and died there in 1925.

The Great Imitator

Leslie Patterson

> *In 1879, Jonathan Hutchinson delivered a speech on syphilis to the British Medical Association. He dubbed the disease the Great Imitator for its propensity to mimic the symptoms of many other diseases, including smallpox, psoriasis, lupus, and epilepsy.*

I am a disease. My very existence poisons my father's life. The circumstances of my birth are as unspeakable as the name of the affliction that is slowly eroding his body. Look at how Manet, this man that I have been taught to call my godfather, my *parain,* cringes as I help him with his stylish dress. I reach my arms about him to tie his cravat, and he shrinks away from my almost embrace.

Although I have been a financial broker for years, when I make my regular visits to my *parain's* apartment, I am still relegated to being his body servant, dressing him for his evening forays and often accompanying him. Tonight he is going to a demonstration of some dubious new cure for the pox, the disease that everyone knows about but that polite society chooses not to acknowledge. So, who better to accompany the artist to this *soirée* than Manet's other secret? I, his *enfant naturel.*

When I am through with my *parain's toilette,* I stand back from him so that he can examine himself, standing alone, in the cheval mirror. Ever since he suffered that sudden paralysis outside his studio four years ago, he does not like to see himself alongside young men. With the help of the building's garlicky concierge, Aristide, I had scooped the artist off the sidewalk. He has resented poor Aristide's good health and, I daresay, mine, ever since. Young men, healthy men, remind my *parain* of all that he has lost.

His disintegration is most painful because it is public. For him, there have always been two lives, that of the private man, with all his needs and frailties, and that of the dazzling, handsome, and witty public man. It is shameful for him when the lives become muddled. Last week, I handed him the *Paris Illustrée.* To accompany an article on *le beau monde,* the journal had printed an engraving of the thirteen-year-old portrait his friend Fantin had painted of him. It was the portrait once dubbed "the blond, the smiling Manet," the one where he looks as fresh as a rain-washed morning. My *parain* took one look at the paper, then shuffled over to the grate and stuck it in the fire. "That's a cruel joke," he said.

The night smells of autumn, coal smoke and wet leaves. We ride in a hired cab beneath the streetlamps. To break the silence between us, I whistle a tune.

Manet must know it. My *parain* was once a great walker, a *boulevardier* who could tramp half the streets of Paris in a day. He would have heard this ditty while strolling past a group of bandy-legged sailors or under a builder's scaffold. It is in a register that even the roughest voice can reach.

His reaction is not what I expect: he sings. *"But who gives a damn if you get syphilis so long as you get laid?"* He chuckles at the low lyrics. "Leon, never base your life on the foolish advice of a street song."

His paternal tone insults me. It is late in the day for him to play the role of father. I am thirty years old and a bachelor, but no saint. This man of the world concerns himself so little with my life that he never guesses how I take precautions: frequenting only the government inspected brothels, and after release wrapping my penis in silk soaked with wine and shavings of wood from the guaiac tree.

The carriage stops in front of a massive apartment that was built probably twenty years ago during Haussmann's heyday. Its gray stone weeps with rain. The conservative architecture gives no clue as to what will go on inside. What, pray tell, will cure the pox tonight? Mercury pills? Injections with serums derived from guinea pigs? A new diet?

My *parain* grabs my arm as he steps out of the carriage, then slides his bad leg under him. As I bang the door's iron knocker, I can feel his sickly body shivering. We are shown into a sitting room that is crowded with potted palms and silent men in topcoats. Once my eyes adjust to the glare of the yellow gas light, I see that the room is full of the usual crowd: the infirm and their hired lackeys.

Like Manet, most of the diseased lean heavily on canes. For them, walking sticks are no mere accessory. Standing, these men favor one leg or the other, and, when seated, their afflicted legs assume curious wooden poses, or thump the air frantically. One man, with a face as red as his hair, reminds me of an Irish Setter scratching for fleas. I think I know him but realize that it is only his eyes that are familiar. The redhead has the drooping lids and dilated pupils of a morphine addict.

For a few of the other occupants of the room, the malady has taken a different route and traveled up the spine to the brain. These invalids have beads of moisture at the corners of their lax mouths, and they stare off into the distance with looks of unfocused fury. I wonder if these men have forgotten the causes of their anger. Perhaps, I think, they are unable to remember how to wipe the unhappy expressions from their faces, just as they are incapable of wiping the spittle from their mouths. The judge, Manet's father, ended up like these old men, angry and insane. His family propped him up in a chair with his red ribbon of the Legion of Honor pinned to his chest, and for twelve years, Manet used this incontinent puppet's displeasure as an excuse to not marry my "sister" Suzanne. A plump Dutch woman who had been hired to teach the artist and his brothers piano was hardly a fitting match for the eldest son of the syphilitic judge, Auguste Manet. Is mad Auguste still clenching his jaw in that censorious manner in his grave, thinking of his son's marriage to this commoner? Or does his skull smile with the knowledge that when Suzanne and the artist finally married, I was eleven years old, too old to be legitimized without setting tongues wagging?

Tonight, all of the ill, sane and insane, avoid a strange piece of equipment that waits in the center of the room. The thing is composed of two evenly spaced, high metal bars. Suspended from the bars and attached to a winch is a leather contraption that resembles a pony's harness.

A short, bald man with an immaculate white goatee enters the room and steps up to the machine. He claps his hands officiously, as if he must cut through chatter to get our attention. "Thank you, gentlemen, for coming to witness the miracle of science that is known as the Seyre Suspension. In case after case, no treatment has proven to be more efficacious in the eradication of disease. May I have a volunteer to demonstrate this marvelous device?"

There is not one raised hand in the room, and a bit of nervous laughter travels among the sentient.

"No one?" A look, too stern to be called disappointment, crosses the bald doctor's face. "Not one of you ready to be cured?"

Gradually, a gray-haired codger who looks quite out of his mind is prodded towards the machine by an earnest young man. "My father will try," the young man says.

The father, who is perhaps not as mad as I had guessed, tries to claw his way through the assembled crowd to the door, but two thugs in white jackets grab his shriveled arms and lift his jittery body into place below the terrible machine. With mechanical speed, the thugs fasten the strap of the harness underneath the victim's chin and begin to winch his body into the air. The old man's body, suspended only by the chin, does a kind of hanged man's jig. His feet struggle to find purchase in the empty air below him. The doctor with the white goatee explains that the Seyre Suspension is working, realigning the old man's spine in a most salubrious manner.

As the victim's face turns red and his eyes cloud up with tears, the son who has inflicted this punishment on his old man winces. "Isn't it time that my father is set down now?"

"No. No. The procedure's healthful effects are only beginning to be felt. Four minutes, five minutes will do your father a world of good."

To distract myself from the suspended man's liver colored jaw and bulging eyes, I watch my *parain's* face. Manet appraises the spectacle, absorbing each grunt of anguish, each twitching limb. Once when my *parain* was painting a Christ with angels, I heard him say that no image, heroic or erotic, could ever measure up to the image of pain. "Pain. That's the core of humanity. That is the poem," he rhapsodized. I doubted him then. I've always felt that the only pain that the artist appreciates is his own. To me, even Manet's wounded Christ looks curiously like a self-portrait.

Certainly my *parain* has never sensed my pain fully enough to come to my rescue. I suppose people think he is generous. There was the little apartment he rented for my "sister" Suzanne after I came along. There was my tuition as a boarder at the Institution Marc-Dastes. And yes, when I was a lonely little boy there, I did long for Thursdays and Sundays when my godfather, the radiant Manet, would climb the school's marble staircase to take me ice-skating in winter or to the park in summer. But what about that time in the park when the music played—the day with his mother, and Suzanne, and a hundred other people and two cruel little girls in summer dresses? The girls were beautiful in their dresses with the short puffy sleeves, and I played with them happily for a while, until they asked me who my father was. I still remember the way I suddenly became red and panicky. I knew that my last name was Leenhoff, like Suzanne's, but I had no idea about my father. I had been told he was in Holland, but I had never met him. Noting my confusion, the girls began a chorus of teasing. I picked up a piece of gravel and threw it. The stone hit the blond girl on her arm. The sting of the impact made her stop her teasing, but the blood, appearing so sudden and scarlet next to her white dress, made her cry. I ran away from her wailing. I ran to the first comforting presence I set eyes on, Manet in his glossy top hat. I rushed towards my *parain's* circle of light, but the instant I came near, he pushed me aside into the arms of his mother. From Mme. Manet's lap, my teary eyes noted that the artist's hands held paper. He had been sketching the awful girls the whole time. And when Manet's mother finally dried my eyes and set me down onto the ground with a reprimand, he sketched that, too. Twenty years later, his canvas *Music in the Tuileries,* forces me to relive that day again and again. In a sense, that moment when I was out of tune with the rest of humanity, in torment while the rest of the world seemed to be laughing, became the signature of my life.

As for this latest poem of pain, the spectacle of the Seyre Suspension, it is a distended five minutes before the insane old man is reeled down from the heights and the harness is removed from his chafed jaw. His abused white body falls to the floor in a quivering heap. The victim's son hovers over him. Why is it impossible for me to imagine myself fluttering over Manet's body, the tails of my gray coat spread like pigeon wings? If this foolish son's love for a father was able to evince such a demonstration of pain, what would the confused mass of emotion I hold for Manet unleash?

Summer passes in a blur of shower baths and trains. On Friday afternoons, I leave my brokerage to ride the rails out to Bellevue where my *parain* is taking the water cure.

It is a wet summer, and the rain makes Manet peevish. He hasn't the strength to paint, and Suzanne's clucking presence annoys him, so he writes letters to his many female admirers. The missives to his old friend Mery Laurent, the voluptuous and scandalous actress, are long and, I suspect, confessional, while the dainty notes that he sends to the debutante Isabelle Lemonier are filled with flirtatious rhymes and sketches. He asks me to mail them as if I am too stupid to sense the slight these attentive letters contain towards Suzanne and, by extension, to myself. I slip them in the post and feel that I have become my syphilitic father's panderer.

But the water cure, the point of Manet's visit to Bellevue, is by far the most undignified aspect of the summer. It consists of a succession of hot and cold showers and pummeling massages designed to root out every ill. But my *parain* complains so much about the rough treatment meted out to him by the rural attendants at the spa that I drape a towel over my arm to see to his comfort myself.

The baths have the atmosphere of a sterile, white-tiled cave. The air is clammy, and the voices coming from the showers have the quality of the ocean trapped in the chambers of a shell. A Russian lets out an exasperated cry, followed by a hoarse laugh. Dull thwacks come from a room where a valet massages the blue-tinged skin of his master. The wheels on a passing bathchair need oiling.

It is safe to concentrate on the sounds. It is the only way to block out the distressing whiteness of my *parain's* body. There he leans with his forehead against the shower wall, looking twice his fifty years. I despise the way this cure makes us so intimate. I despise my growing familiarity with his naked, weak body. His pale, twig-like left leg horrifies me. And even though I make a point of focusing on the swirl of his thinning hair around his scalp, I feel my eyes continually drawn to his sex, searching the shriveled member for a trace of the old chancre that marked the start of his disease. When did he catch it? When he sailed to Rio as a young man? It is so convenient to blame other countries for our diseases. We French call it the Italian Sickness while the Germans call it the Spanish Itch. And long ago, it was even known as the Canton Rash.

"Help me dry off."

I kneel on the wet tiles, and Manet gives me a dismayed look. Is it the way the knees of my trousers are suddenly sodden or is it my trousers themselves that have provoked him? I suddenly see that the check of their houndstooth is much too strident. Thinking how Manet would never own such a hideous article of clothing, I begin to attack the artist with my towel.

"Not so hard," my *parain* shouts. Then, realizing that he has been too rough on me, he tries to make a joke of things: "I worry that the louts outside might have taught you their technique."

I laugh in response and hate myself for the concession. If I were to ally myself with the bumpkins and valets who hang about the spa's courtyard smoking and flirting with the laundresses who wash the towels, Manet would only have himself to blame. With one stroke of the pen, with one public announcement that I was his son, he could have raised me far above such society. Other shamed fathers have done it. And such a gesture would have raised my aspirations above the world of business. I probably would have stayed on in school. Now, wouldn't my *parain* suffer in the estimation of all his fine friends if I were to slip that small, almost imperceptible bit in rank, and become one of the rabble? It would be another item for the lovely ladies to whisper about behind their gloved hands.

Manet goes into the tepidarium for his next immersion, and I head for the courtyard. I join a group of men smoking, but their conversation turns as threadbare as their collars when I enter the cluster. There are class lines even between valets and failing stockbrokers. To ease the situation, I rest my lit cigarette on a windowsill and wink at the group of liveried men. "Would you like to meet a famous artist?" I say, as I remove my coat.

The men start guffawing in anticipation, and my athletic figure even attracts the attention of the laundresses. They pause in their work of washing the endless white towels used in the water cure, to watch me. I bow towards the prettiest of the girls and am pleased to notice a blush travel from the girl's cheeks to her bare arms to her rough little hands.

Stepping to the center of the courtyard, I announce, "Voila, Monsieur Manet dances the pox polka."

The audience titters as I transform into my godfather. My posture becomes stooped. The healthy light in my eyes grows dull. My smile turns downward in a grimace of pain. Suddenly my left leg slips out from beneath me. I look at the appendage with wild-eyed dismay. I use my left arm to push the leg back towards its partner, but then the leg begins jumping up and down as if it is operating a knifegrinder's wheel.

My audience laughs and shouts encouragement. "Dance, dance, dance," one young man chants.

I clutch the furiously pumping leg with both my hands. When the leg stops its apoplectic jig, I eye it mistrustfully. And, sure enough, the instant I remove my gaze from the disobedient leg, it begins its frantic dancing once more.

The girls shriek with laughter and their bosoms heave underneath their round-necked chemises. I end my performance with a groan and widen my legs slowly into the full splits of a tired acrobat.

With the sound of the riffraff's applause still in my ears, I fold a fresh towel over my arm and go to fetch the real Manet.

In his paintings, my *parain* has twice cast me as a serving boy. He assigns me an equally servile role in his life. Consequently, I am the one to accompany him to the homeopath who prescribes the ergot. I am the one to mix up the nasty stuff, a fungus that smells like rye bread and dusty feet, and I am the one to feed it to him. Two months later, I am the first one to peel back the sheet of the bed to which he has taken and look at his left leg gone black and cheesy with gangrene. Finally, I am the one to arrange the amputation, inviting in the three butchers— Siredy, Tillaux, and Marjolin—to do the work. His screams are horrible. Two minutes into the procedure, I only want my *parain* to lose consciousness, so I don't have to hear him any more.

The night after the operation, I take over the watch from Suzanne and sit beside my *parain's* feverish and unconscious body. Manet looks like a corpse, his cheeks as sharp as elbows. His breath comes in wheezing gasps, and in an awful moment, I imagine killing him. Would anyone know if I were to place a pillow over those staccato breaths? In killing him, I would surely release my *parain* from the tight fist of pain, but it is doubtful that the murder would unchain me from the grip of feeling. I do nothing.

My *parain* is more famous than we knew. Abbe Hurel visits, telling me that the Archbishop of Paris himself has offered to administer the last rites.

"I do not see the necessity," I say.

"But surely you see that Manet is dying," the Abbe pleads.

"Perhaps. But he has scarcely been a believer."

"Pain is often a path to the Father."

The Abbe's sentence strikes me like a slap. "If my *parain* shows any sign of desiring the last sacrament, you can be assured that I will call you. But as for suggesting such a thing, I can't do it."

The air in Manet's room is swampy and breathtaking. The rot has obviously traveled beyond his leg. Although the April weather is unseasonably warm, he shivers. I do not light a fire for fear that the heat will intensify the abattoir stench of his body.

Seven nights after the amputation, while Manet is shifting in and out of delirium, I discover that my *parain's* amputated leg has been left in the sickroom fireplace to fester behind an andiron. Did those foolish surgeons simply forget to dispose of it properly, or did they think that I, a mere godson, would feel nothing as I watched Manet's dried out appendage fizzle and pop in the flames?

I cover my nose and mouth with a nearby towel and grab the swarming black mass with the fireplace tongs. The surprising weight of the limb causes me to drop it, scattering maggots on the tile mantle. I curse and delicately lift the limb again, this time depositing it into the coal scuttle. I sob with frustration and horror.

What am I to do with the leg now? I can't simply wait to bury it with the rest of the artist in his casket. I've no idea how long it takes to die. And there's no place to bury it here. Should I take the noxious thing on a train ride to the country to bury in the little family plot at Gennvilliers? If I leave it out on the street with the bundles of household papers and bottles, a dog will race off with it, or a ragpicker might stumble upon it and bring the police. I could force Marjolin to get rid of it. He posts a daily bulletin on the artist's health at the concierge's lodge for the gossipmongers that hang about in the street. But Marjolin would probably find some way to make the leg a public spectacle.

"Even now, even now, I wind up keeping your secrets," I hiss at Manet.

His figure, muffled in the covers of the sick bed, seems to shrink.

"You can hear me then?" I say, walking over to his bedside.

But there is no reply.

I build a fire and stoke it high. At two in the morning, when it is burning hot and blue, I place the leg upon it. Despite the macabre nature of the fuel, I find that the way the firelight dances on the walls reminds me of the cozy time we all shared in Arcachon. Suzanne and I had lived there and in Oloron-Saint-Marie during the siege of Paris. Even though I was old enough to be in the army, Manet had sent me away from the city, giving me the excuse that I must look after my "sister." From his guard post on the Paris ramparts, he wrote Suzanne lovelorn letters, and, at the end of the war, he came to Arcachon. There, he painted us with loving, tender strokes as we read by firelight.

My *parain*—no, my father—is dead. I sit in a chair opposite his shrouded form and cry. For weeks, this chair has been my station. While the rest of the household and family, including Suzanne, shied away from his pain, retreating from him to protect their memories, I drew my chair closer trying to see into his heart. All my life, I just wanted to bear one undiluted feeling for Manet. I wanted to see him white: as my savior, as my father, as a great man of talent and wit. Or I wanted to see him black: as the promiscuous syphilitic, the adulterer, the snob, the hypocrite, the critic. I wanted something simple from him, and he never gave it.

Now he is dead, and against all expectations, he has left me everything. Everything. More than I ever wanted. And less. And so my feelings remain shadowed, nuanced, and two-sided.

In the midst of my sobbing, I give a short mucous-filled laugh. It suddenly occurs to me that his art is the same. The critics complain that Manet is overly complex and confusing, that his paintings raise too many questions. A person goes looking for a picture of illumination and gets darkness, or looking for a painting of a pretty girl and gets a nude in a whorehouse. It turns out that simplicity was the one thing that was beyond my father's talent. ‽

Shobo
(Pyrexia of Unknown Origin)

Dannie Abse

He hardly knew a single English word
and was too much in pyrexial sloth
to throw 16 kola nuts from his right hand
to his left. The interpreter grumbled
that he worried about my clay-red tie.
This colour, it seemed, invoked the wrath
of Shopanna, Lord of the Open Spaces.

I was not trusted. I knew nothing of
his gods, their shrines, those tall pillars of mud,
nor of the dread power of the earth-spirits.
He felt himself to be perversely cursed
and could not send for the babalawo
—the priest who kept water in his house
but preferred, sometimes, to bathe in blood.

I was too rational in my white coat,
unable to offer analgesic words
in the right order. Rational? Less so
I agree at night, mystery's habitat,
where a man may think he hears a footfall
on the stairs becoming faint, fainter,
ever more distant, till not heard at all.

Of his near dead whom had he offended?
Whose brooding ghost-moans hurt his head?
Far from home, stricken, insolubly alone,
he lay there resigned in imagined thrall
to some strange malignant eidolon.
I read the negative lumbar puncture report,
nodded, smiled, uneasily moved on.

&

Afternoon Heat

Vishwas R. Gaitonde

When I saw him after ten years, I surprised myself by instantly remembering who he was. In a busy general medical practice in an Indian metropolis, it is common to see a hundred patients a day, six or seven days a week. To remember one of them, whom I had seen only once, after ten years no less, made me respect the human brain anew.

But I had forgotten his name.

"Rangan, sir," he said, and his astonished eyes seemed to ask: how could you have forgotten my name?

Ten years ago, I had a thriving medical practice in the Elephant Gate subdivision of Madras, as Chennai was called then. After the British converted Madras from a fishing village into a town, it was repeatedly raided by the neighboring local rulers, so the British built a fortified wall along the perimeter. The wall had many gates—Hospital Gate, Chuckler's Gate, Ennore Gate, Pully Gate, Elephant Gate, to name a few. The wall had long since crumbled, not from the cannons of the invaders, but from the explosion of the growing city. Today, Elephant Gate was a run-down part of town where shabby residential blocks were entangled with dingy commercial establishments. The city's main railroad station lay south of Elephant Gate. The soot that spewed out from the coal locomotives mixed freely in the sky with yellow industrial fumes from the factories in the north. Those who were content with their lot were happy to disclose Elephant Gate as their address. Those who aspired to move up were more circumspect.

I was just starting my medical practice then, and worked long, hard days. When I arrived home late in the night, my infant son would be asleep and my wife would be fighting to keep her eyes open. I wondered, sometimes sadly, whether I was married to my wife or to my practice.

When Rangan first came into my little clinic, I thought maybe I had seen him in a movie. He was the most dashing, debonair man I had ever set my eyes on. He was all of twenty years old, with a striking face and sharp, handsome features, smooth unblemished skin, and thick, black hair that was slightly tousled. And he was raven dark. In a country where most people would kill to have a lighter complexion, his swarthy appearance would have given any movie studio second thoughts.

He walked in with a slight swagger and told me that he wanted no interruptions during the consultation. I sent my clinic boy out and asked him not to let anybody in.

"Now what is this all about?" I asked.

Without a word, Rangan undid his trousers and let them fall to his ankles. He jerked down his underwear, gingerly lifted his penis and held it up to me. I saw it immediately, the small, lonely, oval sore on the tip. I switched on my pocket flashlight to inspect it closely. In the glare of the light, the sore seemed to shrink.

"Sometimes urine leaks out." Rangan's voice mixed disgust with reproach.

"The watery fluid you see is not urine," I informed him soberly. I knew what it was, having seen similar cases as a medical student and a house officer. But how could I tell that to this young man who had innocently, or more likely, ignorantly, assumed it was a hole that leaked urine? How could I tell him about the corkscrew bacteria within, that, in the end, brought about nothing but lamentation?

I slipped on a pair of gloves, debating whether to slip on a second pair. The sore could be highly infectious, with the delicate but lethal spiral bacteria lurking in its depths. I remembered one of my professors informing us that in the early days, when little was known about syphilis, the English physician Hunter had deliberately inoculated himself with the bacteria in order to study the disease firsthand—a noble sacrifice for medicine, for science, in the true spirit of a mind eager to discover and learn.

"That's what they say," a student had scoffed. "But we know how he *really* got the disease, don't we, sir?"

I needed to be careful, I thought. What if I contracted syphilis from him? But the second glove refused to fit over the first one so I gave up. First, I gently pressed Rangan's groins and felt firm lumps—enlarged lymph nodes—as I had expected. The difficult part was to determine if the ulcer's edges were hard or soft. Brief palpation showed that the tissue was firm.

"There's no pain whatsoever," Rangan volunteered, more at ease now than when he'd first come in.

I discarded the gloves. How was I to break the news? "Are you married?" I asked.

"No, not yet."

"Who is the woman, then?"

"What do you mean, doctor?" He was clearly on the defensive.

"You have syphilis." I was surprised that I said it straight out, plainly.

"No!" It was a whimper that almost rose to a shout. "It cannot be—not possible!"

"But it is," I said.

Rangan's face crumpled up, just like the glove I had discarded.

"I'm sorry," I added, trying to sound gentle.

Rangan wrapped his face in his hands, his fingers tearing at the curls that had slipped on to his forehead. When he finally looked up, his countenance was bloodless; all the swagger had disappeared. His vulnerable side, which we all possess but keep corked and bottled up, was now showing. He softly said that he couldn't have syphilis because he never had any dalliance with a prostitute, had never visited a brothel in his life.

"I had sex, yes," he said. "A man has his needs, and has to give in sometimes. She lives next door. She is a married woman, a respectable woman. Not a whore who picks up and spreads diseases."

I said nothing, but with my eyes I urged him to continue his story.

Rangan worked as a shop assistant in a cut-piece store, a store that sold remnants of fabrics obtained from wholesalers at a low price. The cloth was of good quality but came in uneven sizes. Enterprising shopkeepers could use them for odds and ends. Women liked to stitch blouses with the pieces to wear with their saris, and, quite apart from his duties in the shop, Rangan would ride down the lanes on his bicycle, selling fabric pieces, knocking on doors. Women could not resist the handsome man, and Rangan always made his sales. But a woman could only buy so many cut pieces, so Rangan also began to sell colorful *lungis*, the garments worn by men that extended from waist to ankle. He bought these in bulk from the merchants in Thambu Chetty Street and Angappa Naicken Street. The women happily bought them for their husbands, brothers, and sons, and asked their favorite salesman to keep calling.

The sections between the main roads in Elephant Gate were an intricate mesh of dusty by-ways and weathered buildings, sprawling glomeruli of human dwellings pulsating with life. The alleys were paved with broken brick or crumbling asphalt or, in some cases, were just dirt tracks. Rangan lived on the ground floor of a four-story apartment building in one such alley. Directly across the way was a three-storied building with balconies on the upper floors abutting into the alley. Anyone standing on the lower of these balconies could look directly into Rangan's tiny room.

The city had gone through a series of sweltering days, the high humidity sucking the moisture out of everybody. After making one of his sales rounds, Rangan had decided to rest for awhile in his room before going back to the shop. He peeled off the damp shirt that clung to his skin; his trousers followed. He lay face down on his bed, stripped to his underwear, his smooth muscular body flecked with sweat in the afternoon heat. A power outage had rendered the fan nothing more than a rusty metal fixture on the ceiling. He opened the window for ventilation, though the hot air hung still, as though it was too tired to circulate. A few minutes later he had the uncomfortable feeling that he was being observed. He shifted the position of his head, swiveling his eyes to look out of the window.

She stood on the balcony, gazing directly at him with a roguish smile. She wore fresh jasmine in her hair, and a bright yellow nylon sari with a purple floral design, the semi-transparent kind imported from Singapore. He saw that she had dabbed talcum powder on her face but it was already glistening in places. Her make-up could not mask her age; she was many years his senior. When she noticed that he was looking at her, her smile broadened and a cheek dimpled.

The heat surged through his body. He had to get it out of his system; a shower would not do. Water might cool his skin, but it could do nothing to cure the heat within. That kind of heat, his friends had told him, could only be relieved by letting out his seed. Now as he felt the heat pass through him like a wave, the woman lowered her gaze, then looked up again.

"A respectable woman, doctor," Rangan repeated. "Not a loose woman, not a whore."

"But if she went to bed with you," I said dryly, "she could have gone to bed with just about anybody."

The young man looked thunderstruck at the thought. I asked him to dress; he had been sitting through all of the exchange on a wooden stool, with his trousers and underwear around his ankles. I explained that the condition was treatable with penicillin—that this was not as big an issue as whether he could control his urges. Rangan sounded confident, saying he had succumbed only once when his will power had supinely given in. He had learnt his lesson.

When I suggested that Rangan go to the Government General Hospital for treatment, he refused. "No, doctor," he said. "They'll put me on display there. When I went there for an ordinary chest infection, you have no idea how many students examined me—and the kinds of comments they made—and that was only about slime in the chest. I have no wish to be publicly humiliated, and before all the ladies too."

"I'll give you a prescription for penicillin," I told him. "You'll have to get it from a drug store and come here daily for ten days—I'll give you an *oosi* each day. You mustn't miss these injections. If this disease is untreated, it can affect your heart, your mind, your brain. It can...."

I stopped when I saw Rangan's expression; it was cruel to flog a half-dead horse. Besides, he would more likely comply if he himself bought the drug, thereby paying in advance for the full course.

"I think you should get married soon," I suggested. "Why, with your good looks, you are going to have a line of girls, all with their nets out to catch you." His face opened into a weak grin.

"It was something serious, wasn't it?" my clinic boy asked, after Rangan had left. When I did not reply, the clinic boy said, "That man skipped his turn twice, each time asking me to send other patients in, even those who had come in after him. Nobody does that unless something is really wrong."

Now ten years later, Rangan was in my clinic again—my new clinic. In the intervening years I had moved my practice to Adyar, an upscale section of the city. My patients were mostly from the affluent middle class, and occasionally I saw a rich one from the posh seaside suburbs of Besant Nagar and Injambakkam.

It turned out that Rangan had also recently opened his own store near Adyar, a small shop that sold cut-piece fabrics, saris, and *lungis*. He had left Elephant Gate, too. He had passed by my clinic once, and apparently had made a mental note to drop in and say hello. Even though he did not come as a patient, I was glad to see him. He brought back so many memories of those old days. They were hard days, days of struggle, but it took the passage of years for me to see how essential they were in shaping me both as a physician and a person. My patients then were from the struggling working class, but they were open and unpretentious. I could explain to them in their language exactly what was wrong and what we could do about it.

Here in Adyar, many of my patients were somewhat familiar with scientific information through their discombobulated education as well as frequent and haphazard forays onto the Internet.

"Oh, so from what you say, it looks as though I am heading for a bout of gallbladder pleurisy, am I not, doctor?" one patient asked last week.

She looked at me as though I had to agree with her self-diagnosis; if I said anything else, she would eye me with grim suspicion and doubt. If it was indeed a gallbladder problem and I began to explain the condition to her, she would cast, instead, a bored "I-know-all-this, Doc; can-we-get-it-over-with" look. If I assumed that she did know it all and therefore did not explain, as I normally would have, and, in fact, she *didn't* actually know it all, then she would not have vital information, and of course, I would be held responsible. My Adyar practice had certainly padded my bank account—but oh, for my simple Elephant Gate patients! Rangan's sudden appearance made me momentarily wonder whether being in Adyar was even good for me, at all.

Some people are likeable; you take to them from the first time you meet them. Rangan was like that—and so it was not just because he opened my memory gates that I was glad to see him. Moreover, this time he had not come by himself. He had brought his wife along to introduce her to me. I looked at her with surprise, for she was small and petite compared to the broad-shouldered

Rangan. She was like a delicate china doll displayed in a showcase in the living room. Rangan told me, in a surprisingly shy manner, that they were expecting their first child soon.

"That's great. My congratulations." I pumped his hand warmly. We talked more as my clinic boy chafed, no doubt at the crowd swelling in the waiting room. But old acquaintances seldom drop by. In any case, most of those waiting were hypochondriacs, and the rest had no life-threatening conditions. So we talked more, and when Rangan and his wife left, I told them they could call again whenever they wanted.

The intense heat during the peak of summer—known as the *kathiri* days—can also be erratic. The heat scorches the earth during the day, but with sundown, one expects the heat to dissipate. And it does—but sometimes its remnants linger into the late evening and even the night, catching people unawares. I have never forgotten how I went for an evening walk one Sunday, along the beach, enjoying the refreshing sea breeze dancing on my face. When I sat on a low stone wall to rest and regain my breath, I jumped up quickly. The wall had absorbed—and now was radiating the afternoon heat fiercely, even though the stars were bright in the sky.

Summer sapped the energy out of us all, the patients in the waiting room under a whirring fan and I in my consulting room. On one such summer day, Rangan came to my clinic again. I was shocked to see him. Gone was the new, confident Rangan; he looked as whipped as he did in my old clinic ten years earlier when I had told him he had syphilis. He held a manila folder in his trembling hands.

I made him sit down. It took me some time to coax him to speak. When he finally did, the story came out in a flood. His wife had delivered a boy, but the baby had been underweight and sickly from birth. The doctors and nurses had performed all kinds of tests on his son and discovered that he was HIV positive. Then they had tested Rangan and his wife, and both of them were harboring the virus.

Rangan handed me the manila folder. It contained copies of the laboratory reports, the implications clear at first glance, but I could pretend to scrutinize them carefully while I gathered together the my fragmented thoughts. Many years of medical practice had still not honed my skills on how to console a shattered patient. I often wondered if I would ever master this art in a lifetime of practice. I nonetheless had to make an attempt. I reasoned that parents of a first-child would be the most disconsolate about their infant, so I tried to give him a glimmer of reassurance about the baby.

"I don't think the doctors can say with certainty that your baby has the infection, Rangan. The test they have done—ELISA test—detects antibodies, substances that the body makes to fight the invading germ. These antibodies circulate in the blood, and what was detected in your baby's blood could have come from his mother. When your baby is one and a half years old, and if the antibodies are no longer there, then we can be sure that the child is not infected."

"The lady doctor told us the same thing," Rangan said, referring to the obstetrician. "But she also said that the baby was showing other signs—skin rashes, sores in the mouth, not gaining weight—she said all of these were no good at all."

He looked into my eyes steadily. It was I who had to lower my gaze as he continued to speak. I thought of my son, in elementary school now. I still did not spend as much time with him as I would have liked. But at least he was healthy, a blessing that would be denied to Rangan's son.

Rangan's words interrupted my thoughts. He said the obstetrician had had a long talk with him, and when she learned that he still had contact with the doctor who had treated him for syphilis, she urged him to see that doctor once more.

"The doctor thinks my family has been infected because of me. She seems sure I got it through sex, not through any of the other means. And I think she was doubtful whether I would be open with her about...about other women, because she asked me if this previous doctor of mine was a man."

So he had been sent here for a man-to-man talk about his sexual escapades, I thought.

"Rangan, after that syphilis episode, you promised me you would never go for such things again." I tried to keep my voice neutral, without any indication of reproach.

"But I didn't!" His eyes looked glazed and his voice had a shrill edge, but it also had the ring of truth. "That was the one and only time before I got married."

"Then how..." My voice trailed off as the situation crystallized in my mind. In that one encounter in Elephant Gate, Rangan had become infected with two organisms—the bacterium of syphilis and the virus of AIDS. The syphilis bacterium had revealed its true colors immediately, but the virus had not.

Years ago, I had been able to help Rangan with his syphilis. We had penicillin, the king of antibiotics then. But there was no such rescue from this virus. What was passing through Rangan's mind as he looked at me? That I, the doctor, was staring at a living corpse?

Rangan could never afford anti-retroviral treatment. Even as a super salesman, he must have needed a loan from a bank to open a shop in Adyar in so short a time. The expensive anti-retroviral drugs needed to be taken life-long, however long or short that life might be. Not just Rangan, but also his wife, and the child, assuming that he survived infancy, what with cholera, typhoid, dysentery, pneumonia, and the other portentous ailments lurking in the alleys of the city. And without medicines, Rangan would have to quickly accept the idea that he was going to die, as would his wife and his newborn child. But nobody could know in which order they would go.

Suddenly my practice of medicine had opened up like a precipice on a mountainside, and I was filled with vertigo and fear. My practice now stretched beyond the recording of symptoms and the prescription of remedies, beyond elixirs and radiation and cutting and suturing—it had expanded into something breathtaking, indeed terrifying, diabolic. One little slip, one human miscalculation on a hot summer afternoon, and a life was destroyed, a family destroyed. If it happened often enough and widespread enough, a nation could be destroyed.

I knew that I would be forever haunted by this vision of a dark and handsome young man lying on his bed stripped to his underwear, his smooth muscular body flecked with perspiration, his eyes locked with those of the woman across the street who beckoned to him in the afternoon heat. ⟡

"Silence = Death"

Rafael Campo

His worn-out T-shirt, black as mourning, black
as countless deaths, surprises me—it screams
a phrase I've heard so many countless times
before, in words hot pink as countless
fevers—heat of language, demonstrations,
why does it still threaten me, I who held
my patient's hand who died his wordless death,
the respirator hissing in my ear
the countless breaths he couldn't take himself.
That was years ago, almost decades now.
Today, I see his T-shirt and I think
he isn't taking all his antiviral meds,
the countless pills he piled on my desk
to silence me, my T-cell counts and viral loads
detectable at greater than one hundred thousand,
the silent viral particles that swell
to numbers more than even we will count—
I pause, and shift a moment in my chair;
I ask, "How many loved ones did you lose?"
"I can't count them" is his response. "But one
left me this stupid T-shirt when he died."
Then, we're silent, counting moments, death
counting us in all its infiniteness,
in all we know that words cannot explain.

80

Sick Day

Rafael Campo

The clinking of recyclables picked up
accompanies an unheard benediction.
The magnetism of new passengers
pulls the heavy bus from traffic; God how
particularly orange is this glass
of juice, so sweet it teaches us salvation.
Bell tower of a church, o pinnacle
beneath which she fed pigeons yesterday,
continue your protection of the weak,
uphold the sky, make her in her black shawl
like Grandmother's seem beautiful to me
again. We all get sick and die, we all
remember something as it happened once,
the way the houses' roofs across the street
can seem like books are closing slowly on
the stories of those inside. Holy, holy,
holy Lord, it is February, weeks
from when the sun will blaze like Florida,
hours before *Angels in America*
comes on again. What is left to be said,
the distant war like humankind's first holler
in the desert—do not leave us alone!—
when all we have are these imperfect bodies?
Feed a fever, starve a cold: still, we hunger,
so we pray with our sore throats *Grant us peace*.

ℰↃ

The Hangover

Glenn Vanstrum

Malcolm Hartford awoke the day after the Maasai circumcision celebration with a brain-numbing hangover. His head felt flat and dull, as if the alcohol had hammered his skull into a hyena pancake. It was a new feeling for him and strangely pleasing. His wife and kids always said his cerebrum was in constant overdrive. On this sun-drenched East African morning, the heart surgeon felt as if he could handle but one thought at a time, and only a ginger thought at that.

This so-called family vacation—a safari funded by a drug company—had twisted his cortex into something primitive. The sight of the gaping tusk sockets of the poached elephant and the image of his son helping him treat the ranger with the gunshot wound had led to his decision three days before to return his family to civilization: back to Nairobi, away from the Mara, away from Maasailand, away from any more bloodletting. But since then, while they were relaxing at the tent camp in the bush, something had come over him—the beer, the dancing, the warm acceptance into an alien society, he wasn't sure what—he felt disconnected and yet comfortably at sea, a ship adrift on an ocean of savanna far from Nairobi, far from his San Diego hospital. The sun was shining, the trades blowing, the possibilities endless.

Not quite half over, the three-week vacation in Kenya was, as far as he was concerned, a complete success. Patients and colleagues, transplants and coronary grafts, bypass pumps and assist devices, all had faded to distant memories of a distant life on a distant continent. What mattered now was the immediacy of his wife, Edith, his thirteen-year-old son, Zach, and his seventeen-year-old daughter, Samantha. And the Maasai, they mattered, too—lovers of cattle, warriors too fierce to ever be enslaved, tough men who, as boys, did not so much as blink when the shaman lopped off their foreskins with a rusted blade. Leli, their Maasai guide and driver, had become a trusted friend and resource who knew everything about every animal, bird, and plant that inhabited East Africa. They'd put away more than a few beers together at the party. And the dancing last night—what joy, what a release!

Hartford felt immersed in the scents and sounds of Kenya—the dust, the blood, and the beer. Never mind the omnipresence of the assassins that haunted him: tsetse flies carrying sleeping sickness, mosquitoes with malaria, monkeys harboring Marburg virus, apes with Ebola. The travel doc in California—who'd pumped them full of vaccines, drugs, and fears—was full of bullshit. Last night he'd seen and smelled and swallowed the real Africa: joining the warriors with their wild hair and the elders with their bald heads, dancing, getting blind, roaring drunk. It appealed to something long dormant in Hartford's nature, something once sleeping but now aroused.

He saw that Edith was already gone, so he dressed and unzipped the tent flaps. Sunlight beamed upon the muddy river where the hippos wallowed, half-asleep, tired after a night of grazing about the camp. The surgeon stood for a full ten minutes watching them, studying an ox-picker as the bird fluttered and picked nits and lice from the broad, gray backs. He was in no rush to get back to Nairobi.

Hartford walked down the path to the meal tarp, his gait unsteady. He stopped again to take a sniff of the equatorial air. He savored the pungent odor of woodfire smoke and caught the sugar-sweet smell of gardenia blossoms. He paused to run his fingers over the five-inch tusks on the hippo skull that somebody had perched as a sculpture on a post—skulls and horn bases, the only bones hyenas did not eat, lay strewn here in the Masai Mara—and he saw his wife and children drinking coffee and orange juice under the open green canvas with Leli. Both Samantha and Zach seemed older to him, wiser. They had seen more of life—and death—after ten days in Africa than they'd seen in San Diego in years. Lions devouring buffalo from the testicles on up, wire snares garroting antelope, a gunbattle between park rangers and poachers…he shook his head, unwilling to let the flood of recent events spoil his mood.

"Dr. Hartford, good morning. Or shall we call you Dr. Sleepyhead?"

"Hello, Leli, hello everyone. Think I might have had one beer too many. No game drive today?" Hartford poured himself a cup of the fragrant coffee, added some milk, and took a sip. Turquoise birds warbled in the acacia elatior above the tarp as he pulled a chair close to the others and listened, soaking up the morning. In the warm sun his decision to end the safari seemed skittish and cowardly.

"You said we were heading back to Nairobi, Dad, or did you forget?" said Zach. His eyes, Hartford noticed, glistened with tears. Zach, who dreamed of becoming a *National Geographic* nature photographer, felt himself in paradise here in this northern extension of the Serengeti. He would stay forever, his father knew, if he could.

"Did I, now?" True, he'd promised Samantha, who had never wanted to come in the first place, that they would get back to the city today, despite the brutal, twelve-hour drive it required. And he did need to meet with the Kenyan health officials to broker the anti-retroviral deal for Rolger Pharmaceutical. But all that could wait. As a cardiac surgeon he didn't usually muck around with microbes; the company's crash course had made him only conversant on the subject of HIV, not an authority. And, besides, today he felt so…different.

"There has been no further poaching activity, according to Kenya Wildlife Service," said Leli. "Two other parties already left this morning for game drives. They feel it is safe."

Hartford sipped his coffee, waiting for the cobwebs in his mind to clear. The two days at the village had been a welcome change in the safari routine, though he had come to delight in the early morning drives, seeing wild animals, peering with binoculars over dew-covered stems marked with hoof tracks and paw prints. The savanna was a bone-dry ocean of nothingness. Boring and yet filled with danger, the unknown lurking behind every bleached blade of grass. Each trip there was a time warp into the Pleistocene, and it worked its magic upon him, as did the Maasai village. He had no desire whatsoever to return to Nairobi. Or to San Diego, for that matter, to life in a smog-bound city humming with freeways, to his job at Summit Memorial fighting death in octogenarians at all costs.

"Perhaps my decision was premature," Hartford said. "George Schaller camped out in the Serengeti with his family for five years, after all." This trip was their final family vacation together before Samantha left for college, as Edith never missed a chance to remind him. And he had been working nonstop, all but living in the hospital for half a decade, trying his best to dig himself out of the financial hole the market crash had buried him in.

"Oh, Malcolm, darling, could we stay here at Mara River a few more days?" His wife flashed him a wide smile. Edith radiated desire and pulchritude here on vacation. They'd made love each evening, and he felt closer to her than ever. Eight hours of daily slumber, ten days of heavenly rest from being on call every other night, freedom from the weight of responsibility for the lives of his patients—she was right, vacation was wonderful, and it made him feel like a new man. Things could only get better.

"Oh, I guess so. But let's take today off and relax. No trips to the village, no game drives, just loaf here in camp."

Samantha gave him a terrified look, filled with disgust. She was a city girl through and through, delicate of feature and form, interested in clothing fads, trendy movies, and hip music. Her concept of the ideal vacation was a hotel in New York and nights filled with rock concerts and avant garde plays. Not for her Edith's romantic safari or Zach's adventure travel. Not for her spending the day watching animals tear quadricep from femur. And certainly not for her taking cover as Somali poachers fired on Kenyan wildlife rangers with Kalashnikovs. He wanted to say something to allay her fears, to still her desire to return home, but the words choked inside him.

He couldn't keep everyone happy.

At that moment a battered Land Rover roared up to camp in a cloud of dust, dried mud all but covering the gold Kenya International Safaris emblem on the door. Duncan Connery sprang from the driver's seat, shook his athletic frame as if to confirm that all limbs were present, and strode over to the canopy. His face was grim. A tuft of silver hair spilled from the top of his unbuttoned khaki shirt collar. Hartford thought the man might have cast a knowing look at his daughter, but he couldn't be sure.

"Good day, all. Leli, I am sorry to report that your stepbrother is very sick back at the *boma*. Perhaps Dr. Hartford might have a look." His voice had a strange blend of Scottish brogue and clipped white African English.

"Oleli?" Leli said. He wrinkled his forehead, and a single bead of perspiration appeared on his bald head. He wrapped the red blanket, the *shuka*, tightly around his tall, thin body even though the day was beginning to warm.

"No. Mzure."

Leli turned his face down, staring at the cement patio. Forcing himself to raise his head, he looked at Hartford, then averted his gaze. "Mzure. You have not met him."

"What happened to him?" asked Hartford.

"He is cursed. A long time ago he insulted a tribal medicine man. He has…he has the slim."

An involuntary tremor shook Hartford. The gunshot wound to the ranger's leg was the sort of emergency that ripped the cloth of a physician's life with an immediacy he understood and could handle. But the thought of treating a man dying from AIDS filled him with revulsion. He'd never done it before, hadn't the first idea of even where to begin.

Hartford disliked the very thought of infections. He hated it when his patients got septic. He had never enjoyed studying microbiology. Staphylococcus. Streptococcus. Trypanosomiasis. AIDS. Malaria. Just thinking about microbes made him shudder. He'd chosen cardiac surgery because he liked to see problems and fix them. Infectious disease was a shifty realm of mysterious, invisible, cowardly killers—he hated them. And he feared them. He was a surgeon, dammit, not an infectious disease man. He despised viruses and bacteria. He—

"Please, Doctor." Leli spoke with a quiet intensity. "Could you see him, if only to tell us there is nothing more to be done?" It was a huge effort, Hartford knew, for the Maasai to ask for anything.

Hartford hesitated. In spite of his short time with Leli, he had already seen and shared much with the Maasai; he felt as if he, too, could be a brother to the man. There was no graceful way for him to deny the requested favor.

"Sure, Leli." What the hell. All he would do was look at the sick Mzure.

"Can I come, too, Dad?" said Zach.

"No, son." Zach had witnessed enough on this trip. And Hartford didn't want the boy to see his father shake.

Leli, Connery, and Hartford climbed into the Land Rover, the surgeon stuffing his medical kit in back. When he had scavenged the outdated sutures, blades, and dressings from the hospital storeroom, he intended to donate the supplies to a hospital in Nairobi at the trip's end. But he'd found the gear useful to treat the bullet wound, a soft-tissue injury to the left gastrocnemius muscle and posterior tibial artery, and he brought it along now, just in case.

The sharp end of a metal spring dug through the upholstery into Hartford's rear end, and he wondered why Connery, with all his holdings, didn't own a newer vehicle. The front seats were ripped, half the instruments in the panel were missing, and the engine spewed a plume of oil-filled exhaust behind them.

They sped over the dirt track on the twenty minute drive to the *manyatta*, and Hartford's pleasant morning-after feeling gave way to a headache. With each lurch and jolt his discomfort worsened. Connery pulled up to an opening in the thorn fence and skidded to a stop. The *kraal* had transformed into a different place from the day before. No singing, no dancing, and no feasting broke the quiet of the village. A lone tendril of smoke wafted from a mud and wattle dwelling. No one stirred except the ubiquitous camp dogs and a few goats.

They walked over dirt packed hard by sandaled feet and cattle hooves to a small hut. Leli pulled aside a thatch door, and he and Hartford stooped to enter. Connery waited at the edge of the *boma*, the thorn fence casting a narrow shadow twenty feet away.

It took Hartford a minute for his vision to adjust to the dim light. The stench of excrement curled his nostrils. The Maasai had stretched a cowhide over a rustic frame of sticks and cut a hole in its center. On this crude hospital bed lay a skeleton wrapped in black skin. Flies buzzed in the fetid air and crawled over what looked and smelled like a corpse.

"Mzure?" Leli's voice was soft, not much more than a murmur.

There was no answer, only the dripping of diarrhea as it passed through the hole in the hide onto the ground, and the hiss of Mzure's labored breathing. One of the dogs, a mangy animal with feral ears, slipped between their legs and lapped up the liquid stool. Before he realized what he was doing, Hartford took the man's wrist to palpate a rapid and faint pulse.

"He needs an intravenous line, Leli." The arm felt like a branch from an umbrella acacia, brittle and dry. Harford thought about the gloves packed in the medical kit, but it was too late—he was already pressing the man's flesh. The virus is in secretions only, he reminded himself. Touching skin is not the least bit contagious. He would be fine. No reason to panic. His own pulse began to race.

"He is cursed," Leli said, an odd mixture of love and revulsion crossing his face.

"He is dying from dehydration," Hartford said. "He needs i.v. fluids, hyperalimentation, and antiretroviral drugs."

"He has a sore on his back."

Hartford gestured to Leli, and they rolled the wasted stepbrother onto his side. Mzure felt weightless and stiff, his bones hollow, like the carcass of a songbird. Hartford saw a bulging pocket of pus near the rectum, a pointing abscess, the whitehead ready to burst.

"We need to drain that. Hold him there." Hartford fought to keep his fears and paranoias at bay. This was a surgical problem, nothing new here. This was what his training prepared him for, not the devious shadow boxing of shifty microbes, not the juggling of mysterious medicines nor the studying of archane lab values, T-cell counts and viral titers, nothing but the straightforward lancing of a boil.

He went outside, blinked for a moment in the sun, and opened his medical kit. He removed a pair of purple nitrile gloves, a number ten scalpel blade, and a box of four-by-four sponges. Taking a deep draught of the fresh air outside, he reentered the squalid hut and waited for his eyes to accommodate to the gloom.

"This will hurt."

"He is beyond hurt."

"Tell him anyway."

Leli whispered something in Maa. Hartford doubted the sick man heard. Mzure's open eyes stared over the brief confines of the dung hut as if peering one hundred miles across the Great Rift Valley.

Hartford slipped on the gloves and, holding a sponge to protect his face, ran the blade over the white spot on the abscess. An opaque, gray syrup poured from the Maasai's bony buttock through the hole in the rawhide onto the ground. A wave of nausea ran over Hartford. The stench was blinding, overpowering. His eyes watered. He gagged. He wanted to run, but instead he wrapped the blade in a sponge and poked his gloved finger into the far reaches of the abscess, breaking tissue adhesions and loculations.

The surgeon had worked for years in multiple hospitals with too little sleep. He'd seen untold horrors, bodies crumpled in car wrecks, human beings stabbed and shot and perforated in every conceivable organ, extremity, and orifice. All this training and experience kept him on track. A well-disciplined soldier, pinned down yet returning fire, he pressed the attack while every molecule in his body screamed at him to sprint to safety.

He knew the pain must have been excruciating, but the stoic Mzure did not flinch. More pus flowed out. Hartford wadded up a sponge, wiped everything he could from the pocket of flesh, then packed fresh gauze halfway in as a drainage wick. At last, he surrendered to the urge to flee and ducked out into the sunlight, puking onto the uneven red dirt like a medical student watching his first surgery.

He fell to his knees and retched again, and again, until he could retch no more. Leli followed him from the hut and stood three feet away, watching him without expression. After a long while the surgeon felt slightly better and the ground stopped spinning.

"He needs an i.v.," Hartford said, spitting to clear the foul taste from his mouth.

"There is no i.v."

"Is there no hospital?"

"There is a clinic an hour away by car, eight hours by foot, but it has no equipment and no doctor. Only in Nakuru or Nairobi or Mombasa do these things exist, and only if he pays cash first. And he owns nothing but cattle."

"You could sell the cattle."

"He is cursed. He will die."

Hartford realized the futility of his argument. He stared at the knife wrapped in the gauze sponge. He knew it was crawling with anaerobic bacteria and HIV.

"We need to dispose of this."

"I will take it."

"Be careful. It has the virus on it that caused his disease."

"I will wash it in the river."

"Use soap, and great care. It is sharp, like a razor." Hartford shook his head. He knew the blade would be used to cut things in the Maasai *manyatta* until it was dull, and even when dull, it would still be used for years.

He pulled off the gloves, turning them inside out. There was no place to toss them, no red bucket marked with biocontamination warnings, just as there was no sharps container for the blade. Leli couldn't understand. He might know the Latin names of hundreds of birds and animals, he might know about the nocturnal hunting behavior of leopards, but he failed to understand the basics of germ theory.

Or did he? There was no denying that AIDS was a curse. Maybe magic— black magic—was the best way for a layman to understand viruses and bacteria. Sometimes Hartford felt that way about microbes back home, calling for infectious disease consults at the first sign of viral cardiomyopathies or sternal wound infections, hoping the grand priests of bugdom would cast the proper spells and find the potions that might save his patients.

He stood there holding the pus-soaked gloves, feeling dizzy again, then wadded them up and stuffed them in the now empty sponge box. They could burn it back at camp. Sweat poured off his brow; the back of his skull throbbed.

"Thank you, doctor."

"Someone needs to remove the sponge tomorrow."

"Thank you, doctor."

"Burn it immediately, and wash your hands afterwards."

"Yes, doctor. Thank you."

The hangover, the lancing of the abscess, the stench of the anaerobes and the diarrhea, his own vomiting, all made him too weak to answer except with a brief nod. Yet he knew that no matter how rotten he felt, things were incomparably worse for Mzure. Somehow the concrete act of lancing the pus pocket granted him ownership of the dying Maasai—Hartford's training and the rigid traditions of medicine gave Mzure an official slot on his printout list of patients. He was now Mzure's doctor.

Connery was waiting fifty yards away at the Land Rover.

"Bloody awful, isn't it?"

"I lanced a rectal abscess. It might buy him another day at most. He needs i.v. fluids and antibiotics and antiretrovirals and an ICU and you know as well as I, Connery, he ain't gonna get 'em. At least not here."

"Kenya is a very poor country." Connery stared at him, his head tilted to one side.

"But we have money, you and I. We can get him the things he needs. Let's take him to Nairobi in your Land Rover."

"For every Mzure, there are one hundred thousand more. A million more." Connery, the great white hunter, wore a cold expression. To him, thought Hartford, there was no difference between a Maasai dying of AIDS and a wildebeest calf falling prey to the lions.

"Each life counts," Hartford found himself saying. Maybe he had too much sleep in the past ten days, too much rest. It was almost as though his cynicism was retreating with his exhaustion, and a touch of the idealism of his medical school days was creeping back.

"Rather like spitting in the ocean to raise the tide." Connery gave a derisive snort.

"Spit away." Hartford recalled the lascivious way Connery had looked at Samantha. The bastard.

"I thought you were more practical than that, Doctor."

"I happen to love and respect Leli."

"Mzure will be dead by tonight. He would never survive the trip. You know that."

Hartford fell silent. Frustration built inside him, next to the roar of his headache and the spiraling of his nausea. And anger. Anger at Connery, even though he told the truth. Anger at himself, at his impotence. And fear. He stared at his hands. Was that a fleck of dried pus on his wrist?

"Why did you bring me here to see him, then?"

"I wanted you to witness a bit of local color." There was a hint of sarcasm in the man's voice. "I learned from your colleagues at Rolger Pharmaceutical that you're going to be their point man in Nairobi. You're the one who's going to bring anti-retrovirals to Kenya. Thought it might be good for you to see what we're up against."

Leli climbed into the back seat. Connery and Hartford got in the front.

"Thank you, doctor," Leli said. "I gave Mzure water. He feels better. Let us return to Mara River Camp. We must continue on safari." Leli, Hartford could see, had few illusions about his step-brother's prognosis. The Maasai people, he recalled, maintained no belief in an afterlife, no foolish anticipation of heaven, only the hard-bitten acceptance of death as the natural and fitting end of life. And yet Leli loved Mzure, of that Hartford was sure.

That Leli also loved taking tourists out on safari, that he loved watching the game perform their wild animal roles on the vast savanna stage, was also clear. That was another side of the Dark Continent's reality, an aspect just as potent as the human side. Leli loved the lions and eland and giraffe and hyenas almost as much as he loved his own cattle. There had been real excitement surging through the man, Hartford recalled, when the secretary bird battled the black mamba, when the cheetah streaked after the gazelle. The surgeon decided he would never understand Africa, neither its raw violence, nor its sheer beauty, nor its bitter ironies. All he knew was that these high plains formed a crucible of competition and blood, a cauldron filled by a seething mass of viruses, bacteria, mammals, humanity, birds, reptiles, amphibians, insects, and God knew what else. Hartford's headache crescendoed, a searing white light shining through the back of his brain. A shaking chill racked his body, leaving in its wake surprise and a heavy sweat.

Connery looked at Hartford and shrugged his shoulders. He gunned the engine and drove them away from the *manyatta*.

When Hartford arrived back at the camp, he immediately showered in the canvas-walled bathroom, soaping himself from head to foot. The water ran from a rain cistern perched on a two-by-four frame next to the tent. It felt cool and refreshing, sinfully luxurious after the squalor of the *manyatta*. After dinner, when the darkness came and the generator pulsed electricity to a trio of overhead bulbs, the family drank a last round of Tusker beer—Edith even allowed Zach one—and talked about travel plans. The alcohol calmed Hartford, melted into his body, and softened all the rough edges of the day.

"Our visiting biologists spotted an active leopard and her cub nearby. At the park border, near Cat Canyon," said Connery. The scientists, a husband and wife team, had skipped dinner to process fresh elephant DNA in their tent lab.

"Really? And what do they mean by active?" said his daughter. Hartford noticed that Samantha's mood waxed upbeat with the return of the Scotsman.

"She attacked a young ostrich," Connery said.

"I have never seen a leopard take an ostrich." Leli shook his head, as if to bring himself back from a distant place to the here and now of his job as safari guide.

"Well, then, you should take the Hartfords to Cat Canyon," said Connery.

"Would you like to come with us, Duncan?" said Edith.

"No, thanks. I'm due for a meeting in Nairobi. But do go tomorrow, and have some good hunting—or should I say, photographing." He winked at Zach.

The lights flickered. They drained their beers and returned to their tents. Hartford showered a second time, scrubbed himself again with soap, but knew he could never wash away the horror of Mzure's disease. He could never completely strip himself of guilt for being a rich Caucasian in black Africa, for being healthy when others were dying, for operating on an abscess and not providing follow-up care. As he slipped into bed, Edith rubbed his shoulders.

"It was bad there at the village, wasn't it?"

"Unspeakable."

She kneaded his stress-tightened muscles using all the strength in her garden-tough hands. Then she began a series of karate chops up and down his back until he moaned.

"You've tightened up once more. I thought we finally had you relaxed."

"Can't escape being a doctor, it seems, even on vacation." Half a doc, that is, he decided. He had unfinished work to complete here in Kenya, and thinking about it both thrilled and sobered him. ❧

Prisoner

John Stone

> *In the prison of his days*
> *Teach the free man how to praise.*
>   W. H. Auden

This is the house of Anopheles
in the city of malaria
that infects 500 million souls a year
in this reeling world
and kills a million, so many of them children.
I hear them crying, not here in Atlanta,
but in Africa. In Vietnam.

* * *

I have never before been a prisoner.
But in 1965, I was ushered down the footfall
halls of this federal penitentiary.
Claustrophobia walked beside me
as the great doors clanked open,
then shut behind me.

* * *

This is the room where we commit malaria.
This is the inmate who has volunteered.
For his pains, he will get not only malaria,
but money for cigarettes, time off his sentence.
In this room he becomes
an honorary veteran of the Vietnam War,
whose jungles bred the malaria
now ready to assault his blood.

* * *

The prisoner jokes: "You're gonna adopt me, now,
ain'cha, Doc?" He rolls up his sleeve. "You gonna
get me outa this place, right?" Out comes the vial,
inside it a single single-minded mosquito.
The Anopheles walks his arm.

The prisoner in the next bed reminds him
that he has about two weeks left in which to pray.
That he should smoke while he still can.

* * *

Leeuwenhoek made a microscope and looked
and saw the red blood cells, the spermatozoa.
Had he looked at teeming blood, he would have seen
malaria, too, riding the red cells to the reaches
of the body, malignant spirits, terrorists by land, sea, sky.
Animalcules he would have called them. As for
spermatozoa, they are not officially discussed behind bars.

* * *

The prisoner's disease announces itself: headhammering;
then chills, then rigors that shake south Atlanta.
The prisoner writhes like an epileptic, grinds his teeth.
He expects worse: it comes. His fever spikes to 104.
He boils in his skin in the valley of thirst.
He is a burning man. He is sick. Low sick.
He suffers.

* * *

The soldier in Vietnam suffers, too,
wounded in battle, reeling with malaria.
The drugs for his malaria no longer work.
The soldier bares his arm and his blood flies
to Atlanta stopping only for fuel.
He has three weeks left before his malaria
rises up again, wanting more of him.

* * *

During the past 40 years, I have thought often
of that prisoner, who volunteered to breathe
the bad air of this world, who sickened
with the mosquito, but did not die.
Nameless, unpraised, he became a hero
as surely as that first physician who passed
the catheter through his own quaking heart,
a hero as surely as the soldier still pinned down
by the gunfire of the ages,
who has also borne our griefs,
who has carried our sorrows.

The Only Fat Man in Lascahobas

Evan Lyon

Georges, the owner of St. Gabriel's Funeral Enterprise, is the only fat man in Lascahobas. He met us at the gates of the funeral home where David—another U.S.-based physician—and I had come to retrieve the body of one of our patients, Saintilus Joseph. We were greeted with an aggressive hospitality, as if we were traveling executives or investors visiting a new business acquisition. Georges brought out chairs and placed them for us, with a practiced, somber gracefulness, in the shade in front of the chapel. His moist-lipped smile made me suspicious. His well-fed teeth were crooked and strong, still his eyes betrayed real kindness. It was barely 10 o'clock in the morning, but Georges insisted we join him for a drink of rum; he was already drinking. He sent his loud, spoiled young son to fetch a bottle and some ice. The boy feigned drinking from the bottle and worked the crowd for a laugh, stumbling amiably around in the shade. He had the beginning of a pot-belly like his father. In a poor, rural Haitian town, clearly the funeral business was treating them well.

Georges poured a stiff glass of 5-star rum for David and me, and topped off his own. His wife cut a lime and gave us each a slice on a folded paper napkin. We made small talk for some time, which soon turned to a conversation about the funeral business. Georges' family had funeral homes in several towns and smaller cities throughout Haiti. He had learned the trade from his father in the nearby city of Mirebalais, where he grew up. He enjoyed his work and was proud of the business he had built in Lascahobas.

"Making ends meet can be difficult here in the countryside," he said. His cigarette bounced between fleshy lips, while his rum glass sweated on the hood of the 1970's-era Chevrolet hearse he was leaning on. "Many peasants don't have the money to pay me what it costs to keep their loved ones in the morgue. But I find a way to help everyone I can. There is no one else here." The sun was getting hotter overhead and my head was swimming. I had my doubts about his generosity.

While I listened to him speak, I thought of how, if I worked in Lascahobas long enough, Georges, too, would become my patient. But he would probably not come to the clinic wasted from tuberculosis or HIV. He would probably not come with the fever and abdominal pain of typhoid, since he has the means to drink clean water. As I listened to Georges speak about the funeral industry in a dying country, smoke curling from his lips, I imagined Georges coming to our clinic with emphysema, or diabetes, or lung cancer, or after a heart attack. Sitting among the poor and starving, he would likely suffer diseases more like what I see in my patients in Boston.

Later, Jean Jean, our friend and co-worker from the clinic, told us more about Georges. Jean Jean had worked for him at St. Gabriel's for several years. Between sometimes horrible and sometimes hilarious stories of riding alongside Georges as they recovered the dead from homes around Lascahobas, he revealed that, in fact, the funeral director was a kind man. While morgue services are a luxury that few can afford in rural Haiti, Georges was fair. It is common in Haiti for the dead to be held indefinitely, sometimes charged by the day for time spent in the morgue, until the family can find the money—depleting their life's savings, selling valuable livestock or land, or borrowing from usurious money lenders—to reclaim them. Georges charged according to a family's means, and never kept a body for ransom. Despite his corpulence and obvious success, Georges was a man of principle.

We were invited to tour the funeral home. David and I entered the small chapel. The dim Plexiglas was a poor substitute for the real stained-glass windows, and cast a sad blue light in the room. Dusty paper flowers and streamers hung from the ceiling. They could have been 20 years old, or they might have been hung for a service yesterday. Rows of unmatched folding chairs waited. The green shag carpet, the dim blue light, the stuffy air gave the chapel a subterranean feel. I didn't want to stay.

Behind the chapel, we entered a work room piled high with cardboard boxes and dominated by a large gray metal cube the size of perhaps four refrigerators stacked on their sides. It looked as if it belonged on a submarine somewhere under the Siberian Sea, not in rural Haiti. Various gauges dominated the front of the box; it was not clear any were working. This was the actual morgue. Georges was visibly proud. Before we had time to think, he threw open the immense loud latch.

"Touch the body," he said. "*Tout mo mwen yo se byen glase yo ye. Pa gen yon lot mog konsa nan tout Plateau Central.* All my bodies are well chilled. There is not another morgue like this in all of the Central Plateau." *Glase* is the same word to use when describing a cold Coke. There were three cadavers wrapped in plain white sheets, stacked on the bare wire shelves. One was Saintilus Joseph.

Four weeks earlier, we first heard from Pierre Lucienne that Saintilus Joseph was not doing well. He had been in bed for more than a week with diarrhea and had missed several days of his anti-tuberculous medicines.

As an *accompagnateur*, Pierre Lucienne's role was to bring daily medicines to several of his neighbors. He watched them take their pills, helping to assure adherence to long and sometimes complex treatment regimens. With these daily visits, Pierre accompanied Saintilus through his illness. Saintilus had been too weak to walk, Pierre said, so he sent his own donkey to carry Saintilus back home so he could continue to take his pills. All our patients were supposed to receive directly observed therapy in their own homes; clearly something was wrong.

"How long has this been going on?" David asked. Pierre clutched his bible stuffed with directly observed therapy logs at his side, and looked at his knees in silence.

"How many days of medicine has Saintilus missed?" David repeated. Pierre couldn't say.

"Why did you send your animal to carry Saintilus, if your responsibility is to take the medicine to his house every day?" An awkward silence continued, filling the room.

When David asked the same crucial question again, Pierre finally answered. He began in a low voice, eyes down, speaking softly and in circles. "Saintilus has a house with his wife in our village, but he is never there. He has been staying with another woman across the river. I can't be chasing him all around to give him his medicines if he's not at his house," he said. "I have many other patients and I teach at my own school every day. That's why I sent the donkey. No one asked me to do that. I did it out of kindness, because I thought it would help."

David and I went to see Saintilus Joseph at the home of his "other" wife, Marie, the following Saturday. He was terribly weak from dehydration and a high fever. The rattling cough that had first brought him to our care had subsided; it was the only thing that had improved over the past 6 weeks while on—and off—TB medication. We lifted Saintilus' surprisingly light body into the back of a passing truck, piled high with citron and mangos destined for the markets of Port-au-Prince, many hours away. The smell of fresh limes mixed with the diesel exhaust drowned out the delicate, horrible smell of his fever.

Initially, Saintilus improved in our inpatient ward. His diarrhea resolved quickly, and he was able to take his TB medications. His daughter Jinette was with him continuously, bringing food, washing his clothes and sheets, and buoying up his spirits despite his serious illness. Every night, Jinette slept beside her father on the floor next to his hospital bed. Saintilus also had HIV, diagnosed at the same time his TB was discovered. And though his CD4 count was low, representing significant immune suppression, it was well above the AIDS range and it seemed that he would be able to recover from his tuberculosis without requiring antiretroviral medication for his HIV disease.

But after two weeks, Saintilus Joseph's condition began to decline. He slept more and more, though he did not complain of any specific symptoms. His fever returned and, as he slipped closer to coma, his neck slowly began to stiffen. He winced when we moved him in his bed. We treated him with antibiotics against bacterial, fungal, and tuberculous meningitis, to no avail. Marie, their daughter Jinette, David, and I were together with Saintilus when he died. Saintilus' "real" wife was not able to visit the hospital; she was home in Kolombye caring for five of Saintilus' nine children. We suspect that he died of tuberculous meningitis, most likely hastened by the interruptions in his TB antibiotics.

Whenever someone dies in our care, the clinic provides money to ease the cost of dying, especially when it is one of our HIV or TB patients. Marie used a portion of this money to buy his coffin, and the rest for a ceremony at their home. This left no money to transport the body, so David and I arranged to move the coffin in the clinic's truck.

Today, the day of the funeral, we woke early in order to make rounds on our hospital patients. When we arrived back at our house, we found Marie waiting in her best dress and a crisp white hat. Together, we drove across town and picked up the plain, spray-painted coffin from the home of the local craftsman who'd made it. Saintilus was a slight man in life, and his illness had wasted him to just a shell of his former energetic self. Still, the coffin did not fit completely into our Land Cruiser; we had to drive to St. Gabriel's Funeral Enterprise with the red and grey coffin extending from the back of the truck, the doors tied shut with a piece of rope.

Now David and I waited while Georges' crew prepared the body. Marie produced a simple grey suit, blue shirt, and leather shoes from a plastic bag. I do not know if Saintilus owned such things during his life; perhaps they were purchased for this occasion. After several minutes, we were invited to view the body. Marie could not bring herself to look, so David and I went in her place. Saintilus Joesph was thinner in death than he had been in life. His hair was neatly combed and the over-sized suit was perfectly tucked. His skin was like moist ash. His eyes sunk deep into their sockets and collected little shining pools of condensation as his body warmed again in the hot parlor. Marie had not purchased a tie, but Georges was ready with a ragged assortment. I seem to remember he said something to the effect of "it's on the house" as he held them up for David and me to see. We chose a red tie that we thought would go nicely with Joseph's shirt and watched in silence as it was tied around his neck. We closed the casket and carried Saintilus to the truck.

We tied the doors behind Saintilus' coffin and were off. Five minutes down the paved road, we turned left at *Kafou Flande* toward Kolombye. The path was muddy and deeply rutted by large trucks and the spring rains. I drove slowly, keeping one eye constantly in the rear view mirror, afraid the casket lid would fly open on some bump or that it might slide out the back door.

We arrived to find a crowd at the Joseph home. A mound of dry earth marked the spot under an orange tree where Saintilus would be buried. In Haiti, families that can afford it place their loved ones in above-ground mausoleums, no matter how simple. A prominent man like Georges would certainly be placed in such a mausoleum, grand enough to represent his large financial—and physical—stature. The thriving funeral business in rural Haiti, where death is a daily reality, would support him even after his own death. Placing the remains above ground is out of respect for the dead, a custom that is part of a native religion that includes ancestors as part of daily life. It is also believed by vodou practitioners that those buried underground can be reclaimed by a powerful *houngan* and turned into a zombie. I do not know why Saintilus was buried underground. Perhaps his family didn't believe in such things; perhaps they were just poor.

The funeral ceremony proceeded slowly, suspended in a blur of prayers, songs, and the deep chilling cries of a community not ready to give up one of its own. Joseph's daughter Jinette, who had stayed with her father until he died, was overcome by grief. She began to dance with a shudder. Her head twisted in a slow, smooth roll, followed by staggering which escalated into spasms of pain or of ecstasy. Her tears began, as the slow dance accelerated, becoming ever more fierce. Jinette, possessed, seemed to travel further and further away from the funeral. I had seen this same dance during vodou ceremonies in Haiti and in the diaspora. Jinette eventually lost balance and fell backward into the waiting, experienced hands of her fellow mourners.

After the service finished and the most violent mourning had quieted, Saintilus' neighbors carried the casket to the hand-dug hole below his home, then lowered it efficiently into the ground over two large ropes. There was nothing ceremonial about it. Everyone was quiet, without the usual jostling and arguments and loud disputed advice that usually accompanies similar events in Haiti. Someone handed me a shovel. I bent and filled it with the loose red dirt. I slowly pitched one, two, three scoops of earth onto his coffin.

My mind was swimming with thoughts of Jinette, who had filled her father's hospital room with her kindness and humor and love. She now lay awkwardly on a straw mat in front of her home, arms folded under her, covered with dust and sweat and her tears. Her neighbors still surrounded and protected her. Like those possessed in ceremony, communing with the *loa*, Jinette was gone: her mind far off, maybe with her god, maybe with the dead. Maybe she was caring for her father one last time. ဆ

The Porch

Katherine Soniat

> *"The cold will be your medicine, the snow, a nurse."*
> *—Sarenac Tuberculosis Sanitorium, 1925*

These patients must have veered heavily
when told their lives depended on nothing
but air. Endless, the contortions of faith
they had to go through.

One dreamed sparkling spoonfuls of chill
rose through the pines, nurse demanding,
believe, then swallow hard. The wilderness cure,
it was called, as countless inhaled, then had to trust
mountain air to polish each lung clean.

The sick, set side by side, pondered years of winter
from a porch, bearskin-throw slowly taken for a friend,
fellow being flung across the deck chair.

Spit-cups glistened with blood-flecked ice,
thermometers going from mouth to mouth,
silver mercury, an ally for morning,
risen enemy by afternoon.

Whole systems of belief blew in,
then departed,
notions the mind stirred up to serve till the end.
A sign in the old sanitarium's hallway
warns: *Tuberculosis is never cured*
until one dies of another disease.

What a sentence to live under—
death, the remedial, the goal to contemplate
for months of fur-bonneted sitting under the sky
to breathe wind.

ဆ

Quarantine

Matthew Davis

For a brief period, as summer turns into fall, the weather in Mongolia is perfect. The sun beats gently on the ground, and light cirrus clouds float above the mountains like smoke trails. The wind, when it blows, lands tiny flecks of dust on lips and eyelids and skin. This is how it was in late August, 2001.

The intense summer heat had waned so that I no longer sweated as I walked through the campus of the Arkhangai Aimag Teacher's College, the school I had worked at for the past year as an English teacher in the Peace Corps. All around me was newness; the fresh coat of paint applied to the class buildings and dormitories; the plaque recently constructed for the school's 50th anniversary; the arrival of students, tanned and rested from summer break, their luggage and furniture in the backs of Russian jeeps, their arms around each other in hugs of hello, their semester supply of meat hung in thin pink strips from second-floor windows.

Among the crowd stood Delgermaa, a Mongolian English teacher. Her black suit was stark as a noontime shadow against the clean, white-plastered main building of the college. She was talking to a woman wearing a deep red shirt and blue jeans. Delgermaa waved me over to meet the young woman.

"Matt," she said, "this is Elisa. She is from France."

Delgermaa often lodged tourists in her home over the summer break. It was a way to make some extra money and practice her English at the same time.

"Have you been in Tsetserleg long?" I asked Elisa.

"A few days," she said. "I was hoping to leave this morning, but the roads are all blocked."

"The roads are blocked?" I asked Delgermaa.

"Yes, did you not hear? There is plague in the town."

I knew plague existed in Mongolia, but I had always thought it stayed in smaller towns further west. We lived in a provincial capital 500 kilometers west of the capital of Ulaanbaatar.

"When will the roads open?" I asked.

"I don't know," Delgermaa said. And in the way that many Mongolians in the countryside resigned themselves to authority, she added with a slight tinge of awe, "The police and doctors know."

I had a plane to catch in two weeks. My older sister was getting married, and I was looking forward to my first trip back to the States in over a year. The quarantine and those infected with the plague crossed my mind, but mostly, I just wanted to be sure I could leave.

When Chinggis Khan and his descendants barreled their way across the Eurasian landmass in the 13th century en route to the largest land empire in history, they were accompanied by small, sturdy horses, ornately fashioned bows and arrows, military tactics that would revolutionize warfare, and plague. Many historians now believe that these Mongolian invasions provided the breeding ground for the Black Death pandemic that killed over one-third of Western Europeans in the mid-14th century.

Though plague caught Europe by surprise and by storm, the disease was nothing new to Mongolia. In 46 AD, a plague epidemic killed more than two-thirds of the entire population. And in a Mongolian folktale that describes the origin of storytelling, an epidemic of plague causes a young man to leave his body before it dies, and then to return from the Kingdom of the Underworld with the gift of storytelling. Today, though bubonic plague has been mostly eradicated in the West, it lives on in many places around the world, especially in Mongolia, where annual plague figures often reach the top in both numbers and death rates.

The carriers of the plague in Mongolia are delightful-looking rodents called marmots, that lope around the Mongolian summer steppe like beavers without tails. Marmot hunting is not a new pastime in Mongolia. It has been a tradition for centuries and is a sport with intricate rituals and customs. Before a hunt, a Mongolian hunter dons a *daluur*, a hat that resembles a marmot's head, with the face serving as the cap's brim and two floppy marmot ears attached to the top. Since marmots live in underground dens, the hunter's objective is to creep as close to the den as possible. As he approaches, he will sing in a warbly, clucky voice that mimics the sound of the marmot. The goal is to attract the marmot from its den, fool it with the hat, and then dispatch the animal with a bullet.

Once the marmot has been killed, Mongolians will shear the hide and cook the animal with hot rocks placed inside its belly. The meat roasts from within, and marmot meat is a fine delicacy on the steppe, not to mention a nice change in diet from the ubiquitous mutton. Though Mongolians are aware of the dangers in marmot hunting (most hunters steer clear of areas where sickly looking animals roam), there is often little indication as to whether a marmot has plague, and whether the fleas on its body are carriers themselves. Thus, every summer, Mongolian newspapers run the Plague Alert (much as western states in the U.S. run Fire Alerts), indicating where plague has broken out, and where there may be danger in the near future.

The rumor in Tsetserleg that August was that a young boy had contracted the plague from a marmot his father had shot on the open steppe. Everyone in his immediate family was rushed to the hospital, and the town quarantined, cut off from the rest of the country.

On the second day of the quarantine, an American friend and I walked to the top of one of the mountain ridges with a bottle of Scotch and a jar of caviar, both purchases from Ulaanbaatar, the capital of Mongolia. We plopped ourselves on the rocks and grass and spread the fish eggs over Ritz crackers. It was late afternoon, and the sun had folded itself into a line on the western horizon. We drank the Scotch from a cup, Mongolian style: dipping our right fingers into the liquid and flicking once each toward the sky, the earth, and the fire, before pulling tautly until the liquor was gone.

From our vantage point, we could see the police cars positioned on the three roads that led out of town, their siren lights off, though they still sparkled in the waning light. That afternoon I received an e-mail from a friend who had tried to visit the day before but had been stopped by the police. "They said I could go in but that there was no guarantee I could leave," he had written. "Good luck! Did you bring your Camus?"

All of my conceptions of plague had come from literature or movies. But there were no rats scurrying around town spreading the disease and there were certainly no doctors in full-body suits calling for people to "Step Back" as they worked night and day to find the save-all serum. Instead, from on top of the ridge, with smoke from dinner fires twirling up, up, up towards the sky, Tsetserleg seemed like what it was: a calm and serene mountain town. In fact, the first several days of the quarantine reminded me of my youth in Chicago, when a severe snow storm or frigid temperatures would close the schools down for a day or two. The plague presented us with an unexpected vacation.

When the bottle of Scotch was a quarter gone and the moon had begun to rise over the largest mountain to the north, my friend said, "We're probably the only people in history to drink Scotch and eat caviar in a plague quarantine." I liked the thought. It was romantic, to be sure, but there was also an insouciant defiance to it. If we could eat caviar and drink Scotch, how bad could a plague quarantine be? False logic, but comforting nonetheless.

Though the beginning of classes had been postponed, the teachers still gathered at the Teacher's College in order to prepare for the upcoming semester. We worked some, but mostly we huddled together in the Teacher's Lounge and told plague stories. Everyone knew someone who was affected by the quarantine. A woman who had an interview for an American visa but could not leave. The parents who wanted to drop off their son or daughter at school, but were now stuck. Elisa and other tourists who had plane reservations. Mongolians have great respect and love for family, and the teachers were worried—perhaps just as much as I—that I would miss my family wedding.

"Well," I asked, "Do you think the quarantine will have stopped by then?"

They gave shifty answers. Rumors in town abounded. Some said that up to ten people were now infected and that the town would be closed for a month. Others said not to worry; the town would reopen in days. All I really knew was that the main market was closed lest the disease spread, which meant no fresh meat and limited vegetables; that the smaller shops, the *delguur*s, were still open and selling food; and that the roads remained closed, though, mysteriously, people continued to enter.

I had never seen Tsetserleg so crowded. Our town possessed the only market in the province, and people from the countryside normally came to buy bulk items of food, to gossip with family and friends, and to seek rides into the capital or back into the villages. Its parking lot was usually full of jeeps and vans; the metal rails that ran along its white-plastered walls full of hitched horses. But in late August, there was even more reason for people to be in the provincial center. School was beginning at one of five colleges and four secondary schools, and now was the time to sell any remaining milk products, the food that stocked Tsetserleg's market for most of the summer.

With the market now closed, people drifted towards the 12-store, Tsetserleg's largest *delguur*, on the northern side of town and closer to the city center. Men dressed in the traditional robe-like *del* tied their horses to larch trees and drank juice from glass bottles. Women, wearing thin surgical masks to protect themselves from plague, shouted above the din that they were selling shelled pine nuts, a snack relished by both adults and children. And along the streets and sidewalks, groups of men and women gathered to gossip about the plague, play cards, play chess, adjust their large sacks of flour and rice on the backs of horses and jeeps, and wonder when they might be able to leave.

As the first week passed and the realization dawned that the quarantine might not be over soon, a tension grew in the town. As far as we knew, no new cases of plague had been reported, but the roads were still closed. The crowds still congregated at the 12-store, though instead of the card games and juice drinking, there was an agitation that simmered beneath the surface. At the slightest hint of a rumor that the quarantine had been lifted, people jumped into their vans and sped off down the streets. Yet they always returned moments later, slammed their doors shut, told the crowd the news of no news, and continued to wait.

One afternoon, I went to a bar with some students of mine from the previous year. The bar was packed with men waiting out the quarantine at nicked wooden tables full of bottles of vodka and overflowing ashtrays. We sat at one of these tables, a thin curtain tinged brown from cigarette smoke dividing our table from those in front and behind us, the Russian word for "pussy" carved into the wood. Close by, a conversation rose to a confrontational pitch, and men began arguing and slamming their glasses on the table. I could understand some of the words, though not the context, and I asked my students to lean in closer to tell me what they were fighting about.

"They want to leave," one of them said.

"But they can't, right?" I asked.

"They are thinking of ways to escape."

The thought had also crossed my mind. I had ten days to make my plane, but only if I left Tsetserleg on the day before my flight, a journey that, under the best of circumstances, would take a full day to make.

"What are they thinking about doing?" I asked.

"One of them wants to try and give the police money."

"Would that work?"

"No, I don't think so. Not this time."

"Another is thinking about riding out on a horse," said another student.

"How about that?" I asked.

"Maybe, but it is dangerous."

Any escape by horse would involve leaving at night, and since Tsetserleg was surrounded by mountains, the descent would be doable, but hazardous. The fourth side of town emptied into a flat river valley that would be easy to cross on a horse. But my students had heard that police were patrolling this area at night to prevent people from doing just this.

"If you go slow," one of my students explained, "then you may be spotted by the police. If you go fast, then they will hear the horse's feet."

I had been reading Peter Hopkirk's historical tales of adventure on the Central Asian steppe, and breaking free from a plague quarantine, though not the same as spying on the Russians, held a certain appeal. I envisioned a midnight crossing under the stars: me, a horse, a small bag, and 35 kilometers to go until the nearest town. Just to see what my friends' reactions would be, I told them I was thinking about escaping.

"Why don't you just ask your government?" one of them said.

This had also crossed my mind, but I did not think there was anything that could be done. The Peace Corps knew about the quarantine, but so far there had been no indication that they were willing, or able, to help out. This past winter, a small town in northeastern Mongolia had been quarantined for hoof-and-mouth disease. A volunteer had been stuck there for over a month, and Peace Corps had been unable to arrange for her departure. When the quarantine had lifted, she left the town, and then the country. She had been the only American there, and it was easy to see how that loneliness might have been a burden too tough to bear. I had friends in Tsetserleg, both Mongolian and American, and, besides loneliness, there was the sense of futility and utter lack of control about the quarantine. Basic decisions were not in our hands. Then there were practical concerns, and not just those related to health.

The price of food was beginning to rise as availability began to dwindle. The delguurs in town sold food, but that food was usually stocked by trips to Ulaanbaatar. Without those trips, rice and bread, canned goods and vegetables, tripled and quadrupled in price. The cost of food, more than plague, or the delay of the start of school limiting their winter vacation time, was what most concerned the students.

The four students who sat around the table lived together in a small, spartan house close to the northern border of town. They had not yet purchased their bulk of winter meat, and with none now available, and rice climbing in price, they often ate at relatives' or friends' homes. Money and food were not a problem for me. I had supplies of meat stored in my freezer and plenty of rice in my cabinet. I could always have Peace Corps wire me more money if I had to remain here for an extended period of time. I had worked hard the past year to shrink the large gap between me, an American, and my Mongolian friends. Yet it was clear that if I didn't get sick, I would come out of this unharmed. I might miss a wedding, but I would have plenty to eat. For my friends, that wasn't necessarily the case.

We finished our beers, and as we left the bar, I slipped them each some money. They protested against it, but I insisted. I felt as if I needed to do something. I walked by the 12-store on the way home. It was closing, but a large crowd milled about outside. Horses were still hitched to the larch trees, and the shells of pine nuts covered the ground like brown snowflakes. I passed a young woman whom I recognized as a juice seller and asked her how her business was.

"What business?" she said. "The juice is finished."

Before the quarantine, a new Peace Corps Volunteer had arrived in Tsetserleg. He asked me to visit him one day and help him translate, and so the day after I met my students, I made the short trip to his workplace on foot. The road took me past the hospital, and I realized I had not gone past it since the quarantine began. The provincial hospital was encircled by a white fence, the same white and the same plaster that had been used to construct most of Tsetserleg. I walked along the one hole in that fence and decided to enter the compound to see what the hospital was like during quarantine.

The building was a faded pink color with black paint graffiti drawn and written on its sides. Plaster was crumbling from its base. A small crowd had gathered immediately to the right of the entrance, and above, on the second floor of the hospital, heads and torsos dangled out of windows. The two groups were carrying on a conversation.

"Are you okay?" someone from the ground shouted up.

"Yes, yes, I am fine. But there is not enough food."

I asked someone close by what was happening. It took me awhile to understand what he was saying, but finally it made sense. When the young boy had been diagnosed with plague, he and his family were rushed to the hospital and quarantined. But the doctors had forgotten to release those already inside before they sealed off the hospital doors. Therefore, patients who had been in for check-ups, doctors and nurses who had been on duty, visitors of bed-ridden relatives and friends, and those who simply wanted to shower at the only daily shower house in town, had been caught inside the pink-plastered building as well. And now they were hanging out of windows looking for food.

Some of the crowd on the ground were trying to throw plastic bags full of *buuz*, Mongolian dumplings, up to the second floor. Most bags missed their mark, hit the wall with a light thud, and fell back to the dusty ground, where mangy dogs tore open the plastic and devoured the food. One bag made it through the window, though. It was a straight shot thrown by a young man with a backwards baseball cap. He had been calling someone in the window "older brother," though that term had a variety of meanings in Mongolian. When "older brother" caught the bag, he undid the tie and distributed the *buuz* to those in his room.

The weather had been perfect all week, and the day after I visited the hospital was no exception. The morning sun was warm but not hot, and the sky was spotless. The fires that boiled water for tea and cooked rice for breakfast were sending curls of smoke from chimneys to the south.

I needed to e-mail my family with the news that the quarantine had yet to be lifted, so I awoke early to use the Internet at the post office. The main road was empty. Magpies chirped, crows cawed, and the sounds of jeep engines could be heard driving up-and-down the streets. At the largest intersection in town, a jeep screeched its brakes to a halt in front of me, and the driver stuck his head out the window.

"*Hoosh, Angli,*" he said. "You want to go the City?"

"What about the quarantine?"

"It's finished."

The side door opened and Elisa and four other tourists looked out towards me.

"Hey, do you want to come with us?" Elisa asked. Her face, and those of the others were weary and anxious. They had not planned on spending their vacation in Mongolia in a plague quarantine, and were now hopeful that this latest rumor was true and that they could leave. I thought about their offer. I had over a week to catch my flight, but I wondered what might happen if another person was diagnosed with bubonic plague and we were quarantined again. I would miss my plane. But, if they were right, school would begin the next day. I wanted to be here for that. I also knew teachers and other friends had presents they wanted to give to my sister, a woman they had never met. To leave now would seem like an escape, not the dignified escape from quarantine, but, rather, the less dignified escape from community.

"You know," I said. "Thanks, but I think I'm going to stay. I'm sure things will return to normal here in a day or two."

"Are you sure?"

"Yeah, I'm positive."

The jeep sped off down the road, and I inhaled the mountain air deeply. I realized it was something I had not done in over a week. A quarantine is supposed to close things off, shut things down. Instead, I found the opposite: this week had opened me up to Tsetserleg unlike any other experience in the past year. I turned around and headed toward home. Of course I wanted to get to my family wedding, but the teachers at the College would be meeting to discuss the semester's opening, and I needed to put on a work shirt. &

In the British Library Repository

Katie Chaple

I am the one in the mask
because of dust allergies particularly
sensitive to centuries' old documents,
and, when I look, I see our reflections
in the gloss of the table and also see the buds
of light from the hanging lamps above us.
We each have a box of old letters from a back room—
their folds are stiff, and the paper has the weight of cheesecloth.
I am reading a letter from a shopkeeper in London
to his business partner. It is the same as countless others.
Business is good, he says, many customers
though no new shipments to place just yet.
Family, fine—Beatrice is to marry soon, a butcher
who makes a good living. I scribble a few notes—
though have found nothing.

The other man holds the letters
to his nose, inhaling deeply.
One letter after another he lifts and smells,
making two piles. He doesn't read or even unfold them,
and my eyes water just to watch.
He is tracing the plague through England
by smell—stricken households sprinkled correspondence
attempting to prevent the spread of the disease.

I turn back to my piles of letters and notes,
remove my mask, lift the letter from my merchant
of silks and ribbons, and detect a faint stench.
I ask, and he says, *Vinegar.*

∞

Plague Year

William Orem

The dark came early that year I remember
  ice forming in the soil,
expectation returning to us clawed up in ice,
and widows' weed gone wild unrestrained
  white
dangerous as teeth. I remember Pastor saying

there was something not quite
safe in how the sun was setting, some unnerving scent

that danced in the discolored air. Then he went
as well. We bundled him

in lime among the others, ten, then twelve,
then more, all wrapped in sheets like wood. We never saw

but heard the tales of strangers come
from other shires and raving

brittle words about the End;
and when they lifted people up to burn
                                        already

there was in town a hush and then a voice
no one could ever not have heard again

                    ॐ

The Gift of the Spanish Lady

Marcia Calhoun Forecki

The last words Mrs. Sommers said to her husband were: "And don't let that girl have the run of the house." What proceeded the "and" was a long and detailed oration of how the household was to be governed in Mrs. Sommers's absence. It was September 10, 1918, and the Ozark summer lingered like an inconsiderate houseguest.

Mr. Sommers sat beside the battered walnut camp desk his grandfather had received from the hand of Missouri's Confederate General Shelby. He preferred the worn warmth of the old camp desk to the gilded mahogany table and velvet upholstered chair with which his wife had outfitted his sitting room. To Mrs. Sommers's mind, her husband's insistence on hunching over the camp desk, when the elegant plateau of the mahogany desk was available to him, was an indulgence in self-deprivation. Still, from Mr. Sommers's labors at the camp desk came the profits for the mahogany, so both seemed satisfied and domestic equilibrium was achieved.

Little Alice Antoinette ran into her father's study. The rows of flounces on her dress bounced as she ran. She threw her arms around her father's knees. Mr. Sommers lifted Alice easily over his head and then drew her down slowly until his face nestled in the curls around her neck. Alice's father lifted and lowered her above his head as she squealed in delight.

Following Alice into the study, came Betsy Ord. Betsy was fifteen and thin, but solid as a hardwood sapling. Her hair was confined in two braids tied together at the nape of her neck. Her skin was the color of her Aunt Sophia's dark molasses cake. It was Betsy whom Mrs. Sommers feared might come to run the house in her absence. Betsy was to be Alice's minder while her mother was away. She was a niece among many of the Sommers's housekeeper, Aunt Sophia.

Mr. Sommers carried Alice through to the parlor and set her on her mother's lap.

"Now Betsy is to look after you while Mama's away in Kansas City," Mrs. Sommers said.

"I want to go to Kansas City, too," Alice pouted.

"This is not a trip for little girls. Your Mama must look after her aunt who is sick."

Alice Antoinette scooted down from her mother's lap and circled the mahogany desk. With her finger, she traced the inlay around the edge. Alice's attention remained focused on the beautiful table as her mother repeated the details of her trip from the peaceful rolling hills of Missouri's Ozark Mountains to the comparatively frenzied Kansas City.

Mrs. Sommers spoke in a thoughtful whisper, more to herself than to her daughter. "The train trip is very long from Eulalia to Kansas City. Your mama will be very uncomfortable on the journey and more so at her poor auntie's house. This is one of the warmest Septembers I remember." She looked at Alice. "Aunt Emily lives in a city, not surrounded by the lovely shade trees and cool breezes we enjoy here. But your mama must go. You must stay with your papa and Aunt Sophia and Betsy."

"You won't forget my new dress?" Alice asked from behind the desk. Only the bow on the top of her curls was visible.

"As I promised, I will bring you a lovely new dress from Kansas City, if you behave yourself and cause no trouble for your father."

"What will you bring Betsy?" Alice asked.

"Betsy has the opportunity to live in our lovely home and partake of its advantages while she is here." Mrs. Sommers sighed impatiently. "She will sleep in your pretty bedroom and eat the very same meals you enjoy. I've instructed Aunt Sophia to treat you both the same, so Betsy will have her treat every day. But, she is not to have the run of the house. You will both be under the watchful eye of your papa."

The answer seemed to suit Alice. In the hallway, Betsy took a step back from the sitting room door and swiped the Sommers's stairway banister with her apron. She was thinking that Mrs. Sommers's trip to Kansas City would hardly be the treat the mistress believed it to be.

Betsy had hoped for one more year of school before entering the Sommers's household service. There was no denying that minding Miss Alice was a saving to Betsy's family, and so was taking her meals from the Sommers's table. She knew Aunt Sophia was glad of the prospect of help with the kitchen garden and the thorough cleaning Mrs. Sommers expected the house to receive while she was away.

Betsy longed to read and spell, sing and gossip with her friends at school. Another year and she might go to the normal school at Lincoln University for Negro students in Jefferson City. She dreamed of becoming a teacher. But fifteen was the age girls like Betsy began their working lives; cleaning the houses of Eulalia's well-to-do if they had a relative to recommend them. Cleaning their husband's home if they had no recommendation. In the dairy, or a factory, or the veteran's hospital in Springfield, if they had no husband's home to clean.

Her family couldn't afford tuition at the Normal School, so Betsy could only hope to find work good enough, and avoid marrying long enough, so that she could save money for the cost of tuition. That was her dream. Now she would miss the start of a school term, minding a child, for room and board only. This work brought Betsy no closer to her dream.

"At least while Mrs. Sommers is gone, Aunt Sophia and I will have the run of the house," Betsy thought. And she would have the chance to read some of the Mr. Sommers's books.

What had Aunt Sophia told her last week? "Minding a child ain't work at all."

"But I can't get into Lincoln University unless I finish my last year in Eulalia," Betsy had answered.

"What's up there in Jefferson City for a girl like you, Miss Betsy?"

"I aim to be a teacher," she said proudly.

"Well, here's a child for you to teach. . . I got other nieces I could have give this job to, and more grateful ones."

Miss Alice was an easy child, Betsy discovered. The girl sat quietly for a few minutes at a time, while Betsy showed her the alphabet letters or strung buttons on a string and sang "Ring Around the Roses." Betsy felt like a teacher when she was with Alice. She counted aloud the strokes as she brushed Alice's hair. Every chore, every game was a chance to teach the child a new word. And at night, sitting on a pallet on the floor next to Alice's bedroom, Betsy read story after story, more than Alice could stay awake to hear.

Every afternoon, Alice napped in her bedroom. Betsy sat beside her in a worn rocker, humming gently until the little girl drifted to sleep. The September breeze blew the sheer curtains at the open bedroom window. Betsy watched the curtains billow and empty until she nearly drifted to sleep herself. But remembering the treasures below, she crept down the stairs to Mr. Sommers's library and retrieved a volume of law or geography or poetry.

One morning in the second week of Mrs. Sommers's absence, Mr. Sommers knocked gently at the nursery door. Betsy was startled to see him, still at home so long after breakfast. Mr. Sommers's custom was to rise early, when Aunt Sophia arrived to prepare his breakfast. He worked at his camp desk with as many cups of her strong coffee as he could hold before he left for the office. Betsy was always washing Alice's face or helping her dress, when she heard Mr. Sommers leaving the house, his footsteps loud on the porch stairs. Now it was half-past nine and here was Mr. Sommers asking for his daughter. The tall man looked flushed and leaned heavily on the door jamb.

"Look who's come to visit us, Miss Alice," Betsy said. "Say good morning to your papa."

Alice ran to clasp her father's leg. It was one of their favorite games. Alice would cling to his knee as he clomped around the room. This morning, however, Alice's papa pulled her off his leg and lurched backward as he stood up.

"Not today, little gal." Mr. Sommers spoke in a whisper. "Papa's very sore and tired this morning." He turned to Betsy and said, "I wonder if you'd be so kind as to run down to Dr. Howe's office and ask him to drop by at his convenience."

"Why yes, Sir. Shall I take Alice with me?"

"No. Aunt Sophia can mind her. Go quick, now."

Dr. Thomas Howe stripped off his black frock coat as he entered the Sommers's house. The sleeves of his shirt were already rolled to his elbows. He was bald and fleshy. But for bushy side-whiskers, the doctor's jaw line could only be guessed. Dr. Howe carried an old carpetbag as worn and stuffed as his trousers.

He insisted all the windows must be shut and that Miss Alice play inside. Mr. Sommers stayed in his bedroom, admitting only Dr. Howe and Aunt Sophia. Alice fretted and fussed at being confined to the nursery. She barely napped, and rose cross and stubborn.

The night was cooler. A breeze coming in through the open front door would have eased the suffocating closeness of the house. But Dr. Howe had forbidden so much as a cracked window. He had said to Betsy and Aunt Sophia that he needed their cooperation. He was confident, he explained, that the sickness could be contained by wooden doors and glass windows.

Mr. Sommers faded so quickly. The slight weakness that kept him in that morning was a fever past measuring by dinnertime. With Dr. Howe's permission, Betsy fed Alice her dinner on a table set up outside, behind the kitchen porch. It was still not far enough to escape the screams and curses Mr. Sommers howled at invisible phantoms that tormented his fevered brain. That stifling night, no lullaby Betsy sang could mute the sound of Alice's papa gulping and gasping for breath. Aunt Sophia sat with him and fanned him, trying to coax enough oxygen into his flooded lungs to keep him alive a few more minutes.

Mr. Sommers was dead before one day turned over to the next. He was the first in Eulalia to be snuffed out by the influenza. One by one, men and women from nearly every street in town became ill. The news of a death was often the first word of a victim's illness. By the third week of September, the battle against the influenza had so engaged every resource, every scrap of energy and hope in the town, that the dead were considered the fortunate ones by those resigned to wait their turn to die.

One day, a telegram came to the Sommers house from Kansas City. "No trains stopping Eulalia. Town quarantined. Take care of Alice. Home soonest possible."

The message was sent to Mr. Sommers. By the time it arrived, Betsy was the only one in the Sommers household alive to read it. Alice Antoinette excepted, of course. The gardener died less than a week after Mr. Sommers. Old Aunt Sophia followed that same evening. She had been the second Ord to die; her brother, Betsy's father, went first.

Betsy stayed with her charge in the house. She brought food, drink, and books into the nursery. She told Alice they were playing a game called Princess in the Tower. "The handsome prince is coming to rescue us, so we must wait and watch for him."

In the quiet, when Alice slept, Betsy wept or prayed. She yearned to be home with her mother and her sisters. She envied their being able to mourn together, while she cried for her aunt and father here, alone with a little girl whose fear could overtake them both. At night, Betsy opened the window to let in a breath of air. The curtains billowed. She imagined they were her Aunt Sophia's chest heaving over a hot stove or washing caldron.

When Alice stirred in her bed, Betsy closed the window. She sat in the cane rocker and listened, strained to remember her father's voice: "This is our oldest, Betsy. She aims to make a teacher. She's smarter than the rest of us together."

Dr. Howe visited the house. He telegrammed Mrs. Sommers regularly. The last of September was mercifully cooler than previous days. One morning, Dr. Howe talked to Betsy at the front door.

"Will she come for Miss Alice?" Betsy asked.

"No travel allowed yet. Mrs. Sommers expects you to stay with the child."

Betsy had not considered leaving, but suddenly she wanted nothing else.

Dr. Howe instructed her, "You must stay in the house; allow no admittance of anyone except myself. I can't come often, but I'll send someone to check on you every morning. He'll just ride past. Hang a white handkerchief in the window if you get sick. If Alice gets sick, run for me. God keep us all."

"How bad is it?" Betsy asked him. She craved the conversation.

"Bad as I've ever seen. They go so quick. I can hardly get there before they're beyond what I can do."

"Where did it come from?"

"Papers call it the 'Spanish Lady.' Damned precious name for a killer, if you ask me. Soldiers brought the influenza back from the war. So they say."

As Dr. Howe walked away from the Sommers's door, Betsy heard him mutter, "Bad as I've ever seen."

How many were left in Eulalia? she wondered. Were they all hidden behind closed doors like she and Miss Alice Antoinette? What if Dr. Howe became sick and died?

Betsy read while Alice slept, day or night. She wanted to be awake, to know the instant Miss Alice moaned or felt hot. Also, in the depth of her fear, the words from books comforted her. Straining to understand the difficult passages was a respite from thinking of the sickness that might be only hours away from either one of them.

The children began arriving at the door the first week of October. Betsy admitted them into the house in spite of Dr. Howe's warnings, and her own fears about the terrible influenza.

The children were Alice's schoolmates and neighbors. They were sent by surviving parents or siblings, too worn out, Betsy supposed, from caring for the sick and dying to entertain the young ones. Some simply wandered in on their own. Patients who survived the fever were often overcome with depression and guilt, Dr. Howe had said, too despairing to pay attention to an open back door or a missing child. Neither the children nor their families, if they had any, seemed troubled by putting them in the care of a Negress on her own.

Betsy and Alice welcomed the children. They arrived in various states of cleanliness but shared a bewildered expression. Even Alice seemed to understand that any visit could be a child's last. They sat quietly at first, their hearts too heavy to invent games or mischief.

"We'll have school," Betsy announced one day. "Who wants to sit next to the teacher's big desk?"

The children ran to Betsy and circled her like June bugs fluttering around a lantern.

Betsy moved every small table she could wrestle from Mrs. Sommers's room and the nursery, and carried them into the study. She brought a lamp table from the front hall and the butcher block that held the pie cabinet in her Aunt's kitchen. One morning, a set of twin boys appeared at the door for instruction. They had been traveling through the county with their folks' tent revival meeting when their parents succumbed to the Spanish Lady. Paul and Silas were tall for six years, with flushed and freckled cheeks.

Betsy moved the washtub off an old walnut commode on the porch of the summer kitchen, and dragged it into the study. She scrubbed it up the best she could, but laughed at the sight of such a utility in Mr. Sommers's lovely room. General Shelby's camp desk sat in front of the mahogany desk; it was saved exclusively for teacher's favorite, Alice Antoinette.

The children sang "Jesus Loves Me" and "Ten Little Indians," and practiced printing their names on Mr. Sommers's stationery paper. They drew masks and acted out fables from a book Betsy found by a Mr. Aesop. Both twins insisted on being lions when they acted out Androcles and the Lion. Betsy accommodated them, and then created a little sister for Androcles named Antoinette.

Laughter rose in the Sommers's house. Betsy played Mrs. Noah's Ark with the children every morning. They lined up before her, seeking admittance to the Ark. Each child brayed or crowed or cackled his or her request to come aboard. "I'll have to check you first," Betsy told each child. Then she challenged the child: "Are you really a little nanny goat? Let me hear you talk like a nanny goat." She checked the child's temperature, eyes, and throat while she pretended to determine the veracity of their animal imitation.

The Ark was the top of Mr. Sommers's enormous mahogany desk. Mrs. Noah sailed her animals around the world many times before a dove in the form of a fluttering handkerchief signaled the voyage's end.

Dr. Howe recommended cups of sweet milk with a few drops of vanilla syrup for strengthening the young systems. Betsy served this to the children. The dairyman still delivered. He left the bottles of milk in a wooden box at the end of the street. The Sommers's pantry and cellar stored enough food for Betsy and the children. Still, some children brought onions or onion sandwiches for lunch. For a time, people empowered the lowly onion with preventive powers against the influenza. That belief blew through homes as quickly as the disease.

"Don't seem right me being so happy in the middle of such misery," Betsy told Dr. Howe when he came to check on the children.

"How do you mean?" the doctor asked, sitting in the Sommers's kitchen.

"I mean my little school." Betsy smiled.

"You've found a calling with these children."

"I get pleasure from their faces. They look at me with such expectation. They're trying so hard to be children in this travail."

"That's just fine." He sighed, with what seemed like exhaustion. "What I came to tell you is that Mrs. Sommers is not coming back. She intends to send for Alice. She thinks it will be safer in Kansas City. With Mr. Sommers gone, I imagine she'll want to stay with her family. Has a brother there, I believe."

Betsy felt tears filling her eyes. Without Alice Antoinette, she could not stay in the house. Without the house, there would be no children. No school.

"Come to the parlor and let me bring you a cup of beef broth, doctor," she said, pushing back the tears. "I brew it with plenty of onions."

The doctor sputtered a fatigued laugh.

"No time, Betsy. Just came to deliver the news about Mrs. Sommers."

"Miss Alice ought to be with her mama."

Dr. Howe put his palms on the kitchen table and pushed with all his strength to lift himself from the chair. His upper arms trembled at the effort.

"I almost forgot," he said. "There was another…" He shook his head. "I'm county coroner, you know. We've got disposal problems. No coffins to be had in the county. Bodies piled like cordwood in the basement of Baylor's Funeral Parlor. Baylor sick himself…" The doctor's words trailed off into his thoughts.

Betsy was not sure if he was addressing her. He stopped mumbling for a moment and then spun around to face her. "Sheets," he said. "I'll need any extra linens you can spare. We'll have to sew shrouds and get people under the ground as quick as we can. I'd burn the bodies but the families wouldn't stand for it. Hurry along, and gather up what linen you can find here. I'll tell Mrs. Sommers I told you to do it, if you're worried about her."

"Who is going to sew those shrouds?" Betsy asked.

"Got to find someone."

"Is there pay?"

"Of course." He paused. "Well, let's see. Two dollars a piece, I'd say. Maybe three. Some of the bodies had been there a while. Worth more than that. How about your Aunt? She can help."

"Remember, Dr. Howe, she passed the same evening as the old gardener."

"Oh yes," he said quietly. "So many good people gone."

"What about me?" Betsy said.

"Are you sick?"

"No. What about hiring me to take care of the bodies?"

"I'll find someone. If Baylor pulls through…"

"I need the money to go to school. Lincoln University; to make a teacher."

Dr. Howe looked at Betsy as if he had just noticed her in the room. "We'll see," he said. Then he turned and shuffled out the back door.

Mrs. Sommers's brother-in-law arrived the next day to fetch Alice Antoinette. Poor child, Betsy thought, she had to leave her pretty dresses and favorite dolls behind. She was to take nothing from the house except the clothes she wore.

"Mrs. Sommers thanks you for looking after the child," Alice's uncle, a tall, thin man, said. "She asked that you give the house a thorough cleaning before you go. I expect she'll get nothing for the house, but she won't have it sitting empty and dirty. You'll see to that, won't you? Out of respect for your aunt and what she meant to this family."

That night, Betsy heard the whistle of the midnight train through open windows. She had worked cleaning the house the whole day, without a bite to eat. She wiped the banister with her apron and walked into what she still considered her aunt's kitchen. In another hour, it was spotless.

Then she smoothed the stack of folded linens on the kitchen table. This was not the time to rest, nor the place. Her servant days had burned up with the fever; she had risen to become a teacher. Like Mrs. Noah's dove, Betsy had seen her landfall. She stepped to the pantry. She found two large tablecloths on the bottom shelf. They were frayed beyond Mrs. Sommers's liking.

I don't expect the dead will mind a few stray threads, Betsy thought. She picked up her linens and left the Sommers house through the back door, for the last time.

The cold and damp of the Baylor Funeral Parlor cellar rushed into Betsy's nose with every quick breath. She tried to quiet her breathing, but Dr. Howe seemed to understand her shallow gasps.

"It would be worse if we didn't keep it cold down here, he said. "I've had ice brought down and the windows propped open, but time is catching up to us. Some of these poor souls have been down here for days."

Betsy squinted, so the horror of the sight before her might enter her brain in small, more tolerable amounts. The full brunt of seeing more than a dozen of her dead neighbors lying on tables, on doors that were propped between chairs, and on a dirt floor, some covered, some not, was too overwhelming. The first two corpses she had seen just weeks before were Mr. Sommers and Aunt Sophia.

"They aren't here," Dr. Howe whispered.

Betsy jumped at the sound of a live voice. "Who?"

"Your aunt and your father. I took care of them myself."

"Thank you," she said.

Betsy took one tentative step, then another. She walked between the bodies, laying a set of linens beside each one. She might as well get started.

"I can have one of the boys help you roll them onto the sheets," said Dr. Howe.

"No," said Betsy. She didn't want to share her two dollars with anyone.

"Just as well," he said. "They haven't finished preparing the grave. Hard to estimate the size. No time to measure and calculate. We need to save room anyway. I'm off to see more patients north of town. Pneumonia has begun now." He seemed distracted, as if he were talking to himself.

"It's two dollars each, then?" she said.

"I wish it were more, but the county's strapped."

"I see more than twenty-four dollars in this room."

"You're a smart girl. Your future students will never appreciate this."

"It's for me to appreciate them," said Betsy.

"Ambition can be unattractive in a woman. I've seen what happens in the world. Perilous to a colored woman."

"But you saw me with the children," she said softly.

"I saw." He nodded.

"When the children look at me, I feel important. I want to feel that way again. Valuable."

"She'd touch the dead to make a teacher," Dr. Howe whispered. He brushed his hand across his forehead. "Out of this pestilence we gain a teacher. The gift of the Spanish Lady."

Betsy wanted the doctor to leave so she could begin. Moving the bodies would be hard, disgusting and depressing work, and she did not care to be observed.

"I'll write a letter to the Dean at Lincoln University, when the time comes," said Dr. Howe.

He finally climbed the cellar stairs, and Betsy was left alone with the bodies. She started with a dead man on a table. He was fully dressed, cut down so quickly he hadn't the strength or time to undress. She spread a sheet beside him and rolled him away from her onto the sheet. Like rolling a tree trunk. Betsy folded the sheet over the man quickly, to avoid looking at his bluish face. Her hands trembled as she threaded a large needle and doubled the thread before securing a knot. She sewed quickly, using large blanket stitches to close the shroud.

The second body was a young woman. Betsy folded the lifeless hands as neatly as she could. She pulled a corner of the sheet over the face and stitched small pleats under the chin, so the face did not poke its features through the cloth. Pleased with this innovation, she secured the shroud around the body.

She had earned four dollars, she thought. Train fare to Jefferson City was one dollar and twenty cents.

Betsy worked more efficiently with each corpse. Some were already wrapped in a sheet, loosely. Wads of cotton filled the holes in their chest cavities. Those were the first victims. Dr. Howe had opened their chests for an autopsy. Eventually, he stopped. There was no point, he had told Betsy. The blood-filled lungs were all the same.

Betsy rubbed her cold hands together. She gazed at the row of finished work. Ten dollars. Twelve dollars. Sixteen.

What time was it? Her feet were numb. She walked without bending her toes. A fire was out of the question. Some of her neighbors were already nearly putrid. Any heat would make them unbearable.

Eighteen dollars. A month's tuition and Board at Lincoln University was ten dollars. If she could get to Jefferson City, Betsy knew she could find a way to stay. She had cared for the living and tended the dead. No more and no worse could ever be demanded of her.

When she could no longer bear the cold of the cellar, she ran upstairs into the night. The October air was crisp but clean. She breathed deeply. From her apron pocket, she pulled six buttons of different sizes and colors and two torn corners from lace nightgowns. Betsy clipped a button from every clothed body and a swatch from those without buttons. She would show them to Dr. Howe, her statement for payment.

With a sigh, she climbed down to the cellar again. When she walked into the room, she bowed her head. She closed her eyes and remembered the faces of Alice Antoinette's friends looking up from their desks in Mr. Sommers's library. Best to think of them and not the unfortunates actually before her.

Then Betsy spoke in a whisper. "Let's begin with the multiplication tables today, students. Two times four is eight. Two times five is ten. Two times twelve is twenty-four. Very good. Now, if you are very quiet and still, I will tell you all a story. Once, long ago, there was a boy named Androcles."

Through the night, she recited all the fables she could remember from Mr. Aesop's book. By dawn, the shrouds were sewn. ఴ

The Sky Gone White

Priscilla Atkins

In 1918, thousands more
than died in the trenches
died of the flu.

I've seen pictures
of masked grocers,
nurses, policemen,

who, in their desire
to live, nearly
erased themselves.

Once, to protect
my asthmatic brother,
my mother masked me.

In the mirror,
a nameless sprite's
piercing black eyes

beckoned.
Disturbed,
I pushed my way

through the backdoor
to find the sky itself
gone white.

℘

Measles: 1949

Susan Moger

Darken room.
Wash eyes with boric acid solution 3 times a day.
Grease edges of eyelids with Vaseline 3 times a day.
Keep room warm and free of drafts.

    I am seven years old. My sick room is my parents' bedroom. In honor of my measles they have pulled down the shades and hung a dark blanket over the big window. The wooden radio, with its tapestry cover and glowing orange tubes inside, keeps me company. Daddy brings me a toy phone with a dial. Mommy is a nurse again, just as she was before we were born. I am her patient.

Rub neck and chest with warm camphorated oil 3 times a day.
White cough medicine every 3 hours.
Brown medicine every 4 hours if cough is severe.

    Cocooned in my parents' big bed, I call up my imaginary friends. Demand buttered toast cut in rectangular strips. Ask Mommy to read me *The Five Little Peppers* again so I can feel a thrill when Polly, who has measles, rips the bandage off her eyes, risking blindness.

Plenty of fluids. Soups, broth, toast, orange juice, gelatin, stewed fruits, bread and butter,
cereals and milk, vegetables, crackers.

    The bed table has holes in the sides for fingers to lift it and legs that snap inward so that it can lie flat. Beef broth and green gelatin, prunes cooked till they're soggy, orange juice in the glass with colored balloons on it are carried upstairs to me. Uneeda biscuits crumble in the sheets.

Allow light five days after eruption of rash on face.
Back to school in fourteen days.

    Mommy pulls the blanket off the window and raises the shade. Light floods in and kisses my still-erupted face. Now I can see her—dark braids wrapped around her head, laughing brown eyes, strong hands. She smiles and calls me her "honey girl" and says I'm on the mend. Now I can read and read and not go blind. The measles are over. Maybe my little brother will get them, maybe not. *I* can never get measles again. I'm immune.

Two years later, the nurse gets sick. Fear is on the loose. It races through the house, up and down the stairs. Fear spills milk, knocks over medicine bottles, slams doors. She is in the hospital and, as a special treat, my brother and I are allowed to visit. It is cold outside, even though it is April, and we wear our winter coats. My aunts exchange glances over our heads in the elevator, as if we are not there. In the hospital room, fear squeezes all the air out of my chest. In the high white bed Mommy does not speak.

Notify Doctor If:
Pain in chest.

In June, the nurse comes home. She shows me the scar on her chest where a breast used to be. Her bathing suit hangs flat on one side. She is always tired, but she is home. I start to breathe again.

Notify doctor. There is pain in chest. She goes back to the hospital. On Thanksgiving, my father brings her a little white Christmas tree decorated with red and green balls. My brother and I visit her. She is always sleeping. One day in December, when we come home from school, the tree lies on its side on the dining room table. I know she is dead even before my father sobs out the words.

Mommy was my nurse. I was her patient. She rubbed my neck and chest with warm oil. When I coughed, she gave me white medicine and when I coughed a lot, she gave me brown medicine. She read me *The Five Little Peppers* and washed my eyes. She called me her honey girl. When I was better she snapped up the shade and gave me back the light. ❧

Serratia Marcescens

Peter Sordillo

She kept screaming that the streets had been altered.
As her fever rose, she saw rain darkened, trees turned red.
The germ we grew in agar: the same thin rod
That bred in yellow marsh, in clutter of weed.
Red seeds swelled upon the laboratory wall.
That night, I dreamed of a city older than knowledge,
Dreamed of Serratia, climbed up from the soil,
Drawn over the fields like a long dress

Of dying leaves. A broken city,
Black girders blazing against a jagged sky.
In bloody snow this morning, I feel
The red wind drive past me like a ghost.
Damask lights float upon the hill.
I see the arms of the burning statues reach out.

&

(In 1950, in germ warfare experiments, the U.S. Army released huge clouds of Serratia particles over the California Bay area, exposing thousands. Local doctors, unaware of the tests, reported an unexplained outbreak of Serratia infection, including one death.)

List of Patients
Under Medical Care, for the Epidemic Yellow Fever, in
BELLE-VUE HOSPITAL,
1795.

Names	Entered	Cured	Died	
Wm. Richards			Aug. 5.	
— Long			Aug. 5.	West India Planter
Mat. Compton			Aug. 13.	Labourer, Water St.
Mary —			Aug. 22	
Mrs. Smith			Aug. 22	Water St.
— Mullen			Aug. 22	Pilot
Geo. Brown		Aug. 21		Mariner.
Rob. Smith		Aug. 26		Labourer
Han. Mayo	Aug. 16	Sept. 3		Mulatto Servant. Water St.
John Lambson		Sept. 23		Mariner.
Thos. Dolliston		Sept. 3.		Mariner
Jeremiah				negro Servant.
Mary Riley	Aug. 23	Sept. 6		Servant Girl
Jno. Slatery			Aug. 26	Mariner.
Unknown			Aug. 13	Within half an hour after admission.
Jno. Murphy	Aug. 24		Aug. 24	Labourer, Water St.
Jno. H. Higginbottom	Aug. 25		Aug. 25	English Officer. Died within an hour. —
Eliz. Gantx.	Aug. 26		Aug. 29	Servant Girl, Water St. —
Amos Jessop	Aug. 27		Aug. 27	Blacksmith. Died within 2 hours. —
And. Berry	Aug. 27		Oct. 10	Mariner
And. Gill	Aug. 27	Sept. 0		Mariner.

In 1795 yellow fever ravaged New York City. The 21-year-old Dr. Alexander Anderson became the house physician at Bellevue to care for these patients. In an effort to isolate these patients from the general population, the city leased, and eventually purchased, property from the Belle Vue Farm, several miles into the countryside. (Bellevue Hospital currently stands at this site; New York's City Hall is now where the original hospital—the Almshouse—stood.) In 1798, another epidemic struck New York. This was blamed on the poor water system (open sewage ran across Maiden Lane to the East River.) Dr. Anderson, who had left Bellevue in the interim, began working again at the hospital in August of that year. Within a month, he had lost his infant son, wife, mother, father, and brother, in addition to numerous friends, and colleagues. More than 2000 people died in New York City. By the end of September, Anderson was heartbroken, and completely renounced the practice of medicine. He pursued his love of engraving and became America's first wood engraver. Many examples of his work exist in museums and libraries today.

*

Simon Perchik

And though they're cold
they won't answer to a single name
from when these flowers

covered the air with stone
and room for your shadow
where nothing was before

—what they want is more darkness
not these graves bunched the way bells
still overturn as that night sky

even you can't wear for an earring
hear this dirt making the emptiness
somewhere inside your arms.

ૐ

Coulrophobia

Jacob M. Appel

My father fancied himself a shrewd landlord—he refused to rent to lawyers, the children of lawyers, even a college girl who "had law school written all over her"—but he probably bit off too much when he sublet to the mime. That was the summer after I turned eleven, when we lived in the dilapidated Oakland duplex that my father billed as South Berkeley in the real estate listings. The structure itself was an ugly stucco cube, topped with red slate. But it sat at the end of a row of once fashionable ranch houses and bungalows, shaded by eucalyptus trees and jacaranda. The colorful hedgerows—hibiscus, thundercloud plums, bougainvillea—lent a false air of elegance, though you didn't have to look too closely to spot the cracked terracotta and chipped paint. After the computer science department terminated my father's graduate studies (a parting he attributed to politics and they, to plagiarism), he earned some cash by renting the bottom half of the duplex. The first tenant was a hippie-turned-clairvoyant who conducted séances in her kitchen. Aquamarine had childbearing hips and didn't seem to own a bra. Sometimes she sunbathed topless in the backyard, displaying her generously-oiled flesh to anyone peering out a second-story window. After six months, our clairvoyant tenant connected with her late grandmother, who insisted that Aquamarine tend to her grave in Newfoundland. The result was that the rooms stood vacant while my father and stepmother bickered over money.

My stepmother was for unloading the apartment to the first bidder. She was the breadwinner, after all—copyediting medical journals for five dollars a page. To her, every month without a tenant meant more evenings cuddled up with galleys for *Orthopedics Today* and *Colon and Rectum*. My father preferred a wait-and-see approach. He was content to pass his afternoons watching for his stocks to scroll across the bottom of the television screen, or listening to right-wing talk radio, until a sufficiently worthy boarder came a-knocking.

My father turned down one young couple, a Romanian oboist with a Czech wife, because they were a "baby-risk": "Kids trip on things," he said. "You might as well tape SUE ME to your ass." Another couple, Mexicans, failed the "civil forfeiture" test: "One ounce of weed," said my father, "the DEA puts us all out on the street." When my stepmother protested that the Mexicans were avowed Jehovah's Witnesses—they didn't even vote, let alone smoke dope—my father snorted and waved her off impatiently.

They were going at it like this, one steamy June morning, when the mime poked his head around the screen door.

"I'm here about the apartment," said the mime.

My stepmother made a sharp, forward motion with her head—her way of nudging my father toward the doorway.

"I'm sorry to interrupt," the mime continued, "but your bell isn't working."

"You have to push harder," answered my father. "Like your life depends on it."

He led the mime across the tight concrete porch and heaved aside the warped rocking chair that blocked the door to the spare apartment. The mime eyed me curiously. His name—or at least the name he would later affix to the lease—was Simon Stillman. He was somewhere between thirty-five and fifty, his hair tinged with gray, with large, almost helpless features that suggested wonder rather than sorrow. He sported worn dungarees and an un-tucked Los Angeles Dodgers t-shirt. More Red Skelton than Marcel Marceau. My father struggled to find the appropriate keys for each of the three door bolts. "Safest neighborhood in the world," he said to the mime. "Still, you can't be too careful."

"Turner," ordered my father, turning to me. "Help the man with his bag."

The mime agreeably handed me his small leather satchel. At that point, I didn't yet know he was a mime—and I thought, given the satchel, he might be a physician who made house calls. "Take good care of that," said the mime. I nodded. My father pushed open the door and we stepped into the cool, stagnant interior.

The ceiling bulbs had burned out. We waited in the dusky entryway while my father went off for a flashlight. "Do you enjoy the dark?" asked the mime. His voice was nasal and vaguely Midwestern.

I said nothing. I was a good, quiet kid.

"I enjoy the dark," said the mime. "It's very honest. Like silence." He stood arms akimbo, beaming like a human flower. "On the other hand," he added, diplomatically, "I enjoy the light too."

The door swung open and shut. My father blinded me with his flashlight, one of his favorite tricks. I shielded my eyes. "Gotta keep the boy on his toes," he said.

He steered our prospective tenant through the unadorned rooms, the walls stripped down to their sockets and picture hooks. Aquamarine had left behind a few husks of furniture—mostly threadbare upholstery—but not much. We were back on the veranda again, on the flagstone patio, when my father popped the question: "Are you, by any chance, an attorney?"

"No," said the mime, smiling. "I'm not."

My father slouched with his hands in his trouser pockets, waiting for more. The mime watched a magpie hopping along the adobe parapet, and said nothing.

"What line of work *are* you in?"

"Me?" responded the mime. "Entertainment."

My father lit up—his gotcha grin. "Entertainment, *television?*" he asked. "Or entertainment, *adult entertainment?*"

"Oh, no," said the mime. "Theatrical entertainment."

"That sounds somewhat risky," pursued my father. "Financially speaking, I mean."

"Maybe. It can be."

My father went in for the kill. "And your employer is...?"

"Myself. I perform mime at the zoo."

Even at the age of eleven, I recognized this to be a fatal admission. He might as well have confessed to gun-running or pedophilia. Aquamarine, at least, had been a fortune teller *with a trust fund*. But my father looked up suddenly, like a man pierced by an arrow. My stepmother glared down from their bedroom window—her hair wrapped in a kerchief, her small, sharp features like blades. My father shifted his weight uncomfortably and examined the flagstones.

"You'll pay for the first month in advance?" he asked.

"Depends how much it is," answered the mime.

"Of course, that's a given," conceded my father. He appeared to have rapidly warmed to the idea of renting to the mime. "We'll go inside and figure out something reasonable."

"I do hope so," said the mime.

"I wanted to be a mime once," said my father. "But I talked myself out of it."

The mime did not laugh. "It's hard work," he said.

"I don't doubt that," agreed my father. "Mime is money."

Our new tenant retrieved his wallet from his back pocket. He redeemed his satchel with a five-dollar bill.

Later that evening—after the mime and my father had negotiated a "fair" price—I watched from behind the front curtains as Simon repeatedly pressed the broken doorbell. He had no way of knowing that the coils had rusted through, so he pushed with full force—as though poking out an eye. He tried using the tip of a broken branch, then the point of a baby-blue children's umbrella that he'd retrieved from the curbside. But when he finally gave up, he looked over to the window and flashed me an unexpected smile. He seemed satisfied, not frustrated, as though his efforts had confirmed what he'd known all along.

After the mime's arrival, my parents' relationship took a momentary turn for the better—much the way a patient revives briefly before a relapse. They still bickered over in-law visits, Fourth of July plans, who was to buy me new sneakers. But they steered clear of the danger zones: money and sex. Although Simon Stillman hadn't laid out the first month's rent in advance—he told my father this sounded too much like a lawyer's ruse—the promise of a regular income lifted some of the weight off my stepmother's shoulders. She returned to aerobics. She let her waist-length, strawberry-blond hair hang loose. And since my father no longer referred to his bedroom as the ice palace, and to my stepmother as Nanook of the North, I imagine she was doing other things to his liking as well.

Watching my father at the dinner table, during those first weeks of June, you could still discern the shadow of his youthful promise, of his irreverence. He was once again the confident teenager who tried to get into the San Francisco Aquarium with a fishing rod, the brilliant undergraduate who'd been recruited to Berkeley as the next Alan Turing. Maybe that's what he'd been like *all the time* before my real mother discovered the caresses of her Capoeira instructor, before the two women vanished into the ether. Or maybe that's just my wishful thinking. I guess we all try to imagine what our parents were like in childhood, in college—before life chewed them up and spit them out. Those long summer nights, when my father volleyed mime puns, offered the only portal I've ever had.

My stepmother must have shared my curiosity. One night, shortly after my father started a new job at the phone company, she looked up from a kelly-green folder labeled Clinical Hepatology, and, apropos of nothing, asked, "What did you want to be when you grew up?"

My father flicked his cigarette ash into an empty Pabst can. "A computer scientist," he said.

"No, Gary. I mean before that. Did you ever want to be—I don't know, a mime? Or an astronaut? Or something like that?"

"Too long ago," said my father. "I can't remember."

"C'mon, Gary. I'll tell if you'll tell."

My father folded his arms across his chest and looked up at the sky. A few dim stars fought through the hazy orange glow of the city.

"I wanted to be a puppet maker," said Sylvia. "Like Gepetto." She drew her sweater over her shoulders. "Your turn."

"I told you. I can't remember." My father strolled to the umbrellaed table and took hold of the book I was reading. *Swiss Family Robinson.* He flipped through the pages indifferently and handed it back to me. "If your mother asked less questions," he said, "we'd be one big happy family."

"*Fewer* questions," interjected Sylvia. "*Fewer.* Not less."

"I tell you, kid," he said. "I should have married a mime."

"You mean a mute," said my stepmother. "Mimes can speak."

"As I said," said my father—but he sounded mellow, almost playful.

A similar mock-gruff humor marked his early encounters with Simon. The mime had repaired the warped rocking chair—his own father had been a union carpenter in Des Moines—and often relaxed under the porch eaves, reading. Although in many ways Simon defied the stereotypes of his profession, the same could not be said for his small, personal library of thespian manuals and pacifist philosophy. He owned *The Pocket Gandhi*, *The Speeches of Martin Luther King*, Thomas Merton's *Seven Storey Mountain*. Also *Mime Time II: Another Book of Performance Tips*. My father, returning home from Pacific Bell with his tie loose around his collar, paused frequently to interrupt the mime's R & R with a bout of small talk.

"Whatcha reading?" my father might ask.

"This?" the mime would answer. "It's Dr. King's *Letter from Birmingham Jail*."

That was the opening my father needed. "You sure I couldn't loan you something more your speed? Maybe *Silent Spring*? Or *All Quiet on the Western Front*? A mime is a terrible thing to waste, you know."

The jokes proved relentless, but good-natured—and the mime took them in stride.

Simon's days off were Mondays and Tuesdays. When he learned that my friends were all away at summer camp, but that we could only afford the free twice-a-week program at the community center—a god-awful experience characterized by forced swimming and long stretches of "quiet time"—Simon established a "clown camp" in his living room. *Just for me.* For three hours every Tuesday morning, he unveiled the mysteries of his little black satchel: settling powders that turned your skin to snow, "beard stipple" to create the illusion of facial hair. Simon wielded his brushes and sponges like a skilled swordsman. With a few slashes of a liner pencil, he could cut or raise his age by twenty years.

We did our work in dim light, illuminated only by the circle of decorative yellow bulbs built into the casing of Simon's mirror. Photographs and newspaper clippings were tucked into the corners of the frame: Nelson Mandela, Kermit & Miss Piggy, numerous snapshots of a young black teenager. The enormous reflective plate was the centerpiece of an otherwise under-furnished, almost spartan dwelling.

"It's a show-biz mirror," Simon explained. "From my television days."

"You were on TV?" I asked.

"Here and there. Commercials mostly."

"Will you be on again?"

"I don't think so, Turner," he said, dabbing his cheeks with rouge.

"But it's possible?"

The mime put down his brush. Three delicate blue stars trailed away from the corner of his left eye. "I used to have a boy your age," he said. "He asked questions like that."

"What happened to him?"

Simon frowned. "He grew up."

Months later, I'd connect the grown-up son to the black teenager in the photographs. "Adopted too late," my stepmother said. He'd deserted Simon for a career smuggling immigrants, earning himself three decades in San Quentin when several day laborers turned up dead in a boxcar.

The mime retrieved a derby hat and cane from his rollaway wardrobe. He set the hat on his head at a highly unreasonable angle.

"What will you be when you grown up?" he asked.

"A computer scientist," I said. "Or a mime."

"Good," said the mime. "Delightful."

And we might have continued at that pace, too. To an eleven year old, at least, anything seemed possible, that is, until my stepmother started miming, and Simon stopped paying rent.

It started one Tuesday morning—about a month into my "clown camp"—Sylvia found the mime and me under his locust tree, practicing characters. We stood facing each other, about five yards apart. I was an angel. Simon was a devil. Every five minutes we were to switch roles quickly, as though passing a rubber ball. When my stepmother appeared through the gate in the stockade fence, neither of us broke form.

"How are my two mimes?" she asked.

Simon didn't answer. Instead, his body—from forehead to rump—went suddenly angelic. His big eyes shifted heavenward. His arms rose slightly, their upturned hands opening like anemones. St. Gabriel, announcing John the Baptist, could not have shown such innocence. I responded with a curl of my fingertips, a fiendish flare of my nostrils.

"Not talking, are you?" said my stepmother. "The strong, silent types. Well, we'll see what we can do about that." She disappeared into the house, reappearing moments later with a tray of lemonade, sugar wafers, cantaloupe balls on toothpicks.

I looked to Simon for permission to thaw. He transformed himself suddenly into a monument to hunger. Gone was his beatific purity, replaced by the desperation of a ravenous beggar. Yet other than a shift of his tongue—which now protruded puppy-like over his lower lip—it was hard to pinpoint how exactly he'd moved.

Even Sylvia was impressed. "Bravo!" she cried, tapping her hands together.

Simon stepped out of his pose. "Go on, young man," he said to me. "Eat. An actor cannot survive on mime alone." He pulled a red Adirondack chair beside my stepmother's and settled onto the broad, flat arm. I poured extra sugar into my lemonade.

"That was remarkable," said Sylvia. "You have a gift."

"All in a day's work," said the mime.

"I didn't know mimes did that."

Simon smiled. "You thought we spent our time trapped in imaginary boxes."

My stepmother grinned sheepishly. "Maybe," she said.

"Would you like me to teach you?" asked the mime.

"It's too late for that," said Sylvia. "Besides, I talk too much."

"Nonsense. It will help relax you." The mime stood up. "Give me your hand." He took my stepmother by the arm and began to mold her body parts—shoulders, ankles, thighs. I was struck by his confidence, the ease with which he assumed this physical intimacy. Sylvia offered no resistance and rapidly adjusted into foundation stance.

That proved to be the first of many lessons. Simon taught my stepmother all of the standard illusions: walls, cliffs, spheres. They took turns hauling an imaginary boulder—which Simon later transmuted into an imaginary feather. They tugged either end of an invisible rope. The effect on my stepmother's mood was fast and sweeping: Overnight, she went from all nerves to nearly happy-go-lucky. She said mime soothed her soul. It made her feel—in her own words—*contentedly preverbal.* The time she'd once devoted to crossword puzzles and game shows was now spent under the honey locusts in the mime's side of the yard, inventing a repertoire of lions, gorillas, teapots. Sylvia arrived at supper each evening as bright as a newly minted coin. She still corrected my grammar often enough—but now she sometimes let slide an *irregardless* or a *very unique.*

At first, my father found my stepmother's new pursuits amusing. "It's every husband's dream," he said, "all sex, no conversation." Then: "silence, at last!" Soon, though, he grew prickly and resentful. Something essential had occurred in my stepmother's life, he must have sensed, and he wasn't part of it. So he complained that his steaks were undercooked, that the bathroom needed scrubbing. "You'd have more time," he said, "if you didn't stand out there pretending to be a tree." My father stuck his arms out haphazardly—mimicking a child's imitation of a tree—to emphasize his point. The truth was that Sylvia's cooking only improved with her new pastime. She even experimented with exotic recipes, *ceviches,* Ghanaian stews—for herself and me. The house was as pure as fresh laundry. Yet my stepmother, in her newfound serenity, didn't let my father's salvos perturb her.

"Why don't you try it yourself?" she finally asked him at our Fourth of July cookout.

"Because it's bullshit," said my father. He flipped a hamburger patty with his spatula. "All hoity-toity bullshit. Like men wearing kilts. If you ask me, there's something very aggressive—sinister—about these professional mimers."

"Do you know what you are, Gary? You're a coulrophobic. A man who's afraid of clowns and mimes."

A patty skittered off his spatula onto the ground. "If God didn't want us to speak," he said, "he wouldn't have given us mouths." He kicked the lost meat to the edge of the patio with his sneaker.

"Suit yourself," said my stepmother.

The following morning—after my father drove to the phone company—Sylvia took me to the zoo. We rode a train, then a bus. Through the fog, she pointed out the TransAmerica Pyramid, the Bank of America Building, Coit Tower. I'd been to the zoo when I was younger, but didn't remember.

First we saw the animals: the cozy meerkats, the oafish rhinos, the African elephants Maybelle and Lulu. It was a foggy Wednesday morning, so we had the giraffe house and the seal island all to ourselves. As exciting as the wildlife might have been on another occasion, that day we both seemed to be going through motions of admiring the exotic animals.

The sun had just cut through the haze, when we finally came upon Simon. He was in front of the food court. He'd attracted a crowd of about thirty, mostly teenage boys—they looked like campers from a church group.

The mime stood perched atop a black wooden box. He posed as a leopard, his entire weight resting on the ball of one foot. An oaktag placard reading PLEASE TIP THE MIME protruded from an upside-down top hat.

Sylvia wiped the moisture off a turquoise picnic table; I sat down beside her. Soon Simon became a locomotive. A butterfly. A tortoise. And then he performed the most fantastic feat—he fulfilled for us everyman's fantasy. Surrounded by onlookers, Simon did the unthinkable: He smiled directly at me and Sylvia. Then he winked.

After the show, Simon crossed the plaza to where the one-armed juggler was balancing a bowling pin on his nose. The juggler's audience was meager—mostly passersby who'd stopped to polish off their snacks before entering the ape house—and it thinned even further when the one-armed performer suffered a sneezing fit. Pins rolled across the concrete. That was when Simon stepped forward, his expression placid as ever, and emptied his felt hat into the juggler's open case.

Shortly afterward, money again became an issue in our house. Simon had paid the June rent at his own initiative on the last day of the month. He'd knocked on the front door and had my father count the bills in broad daylight. The mime even requested a written receipt. But July rolled into August without a similar visit. (I later learned that it's far more difficult to evict a tenant who has already shelled out one month's rent.)

Rather than confronting Simon, my usually belligerent father avoided him. It was easier to vent his frustrations over supper.

"He's two weeks late," carped my father.

Sylvia sliced my lamb chops off the bone, cutting the meat into squares. "Relax," she said. "We're doing okay, now."

"It's the goddamn principle. Here it's fucking V-J Day and he still hasn't paid up."

"It's what?"

"Victory over Japan Day. August 15th," said my father. "You can't let yourself be taken advantage of like this."

My stepmother shrugged. "Nobody's taking advantage of me."

"Of course, they are. You just don't realize it." My father pushed his empty plate toward the center of the table. "You've been fucking brainwashed."

Sylvia poured herself a cup of hot tea. She held the tea cup at her lips, waiting for it to cool. She appeared to be considering her next sentence carefully. "Simon has been looking after Turner," she finally said. "And he's been helping me with my performance. Do you call that being taking advantage of?"

"Dammit, Sylvia," shouted my father, slamming his fist on the Formica tabletop. "Whose side are you on?"

My stepmother began to clear the dishes. "I didn't know there were sides," she said.

"Well there are," said my father. "I also have limits, Sylvia. I'm not running a homeless shelter. If he doesn't pay by tomorrow, he's out of here."

Three more weeks actually elapsed before my father confronted the mime. By then, Simon was also delinquent on the August rent. During those three weeks, my father—for all his bluster—appeared to take pains to avoid the encounter. Maybe he really *did* fear his tenant at some level. Or maybe he sensed something larger at stake. Whatever the cause, he arrived home from the phone company earlier each afternoon—long before the mime returned from the zoo and settled in front of the TV. And then my father lost his job entirely. "Reverse discrimination," he said. "I can read between the lines." Yet without his income, we weren't doing okay anymore. My father no longer had a choice: he had to press Simon for the rent money.

He brought me with him, maybe hoping to play on the mime's sympathy. We found Simon dozing on his back patio. A thin book—Melville's *Bartleby the Scrivener*—lay folded open across his chest. Asleep, the mime's face looked slack and vacant, as expressionless as unhewn marble. On the flagstones at his side stood a bottle of merlot and a half-empty wine glass. My father gave the mime's deckchair a hard, rattling kick with his boot.

"Look you," said my father. "We need to talk."

Simon blinked twice. He rubbed his eyes with his fingers.

"I fell asleep," he said—as much to himself as to us.

"You owe me rent. Two months'."

The mime nodded. "Yes," he said. "I do."

This admission appeared to catch my father off-guard. He took a long drag on his cigarette and blew the smoke into the mime's face. "When exactly do you plan on paying?"

Simon sat up, rubbing his hairline with his fingertips. "Soon," he said.

"*Soon?*"

"You know how it is," said Simon, deadpan. "Mime isn't *always* money."

My father stepped forward. I feared for an instant that he might grab the mime by the front of his T-shirt, but he merely leaned menacingly over Simon's chair. In the process, he toppled the merlot bottle. The glass didn't crack, but red wine leached along the furrows of the deck.

"Soon," Simon said again—decidedly unruffled.

"Dammit," scowled my father. "You'd better."

He looked down at the spilt wine, then turned quickly and crossed through the gate in the stockade fence. I followed.

"Lazy shit," said my father. "I should have rented to a goddamn lawyer. At least they make a fuckload of money." He paced over to the barbecue grill and spit into the crabgrass. "Lazy shit," he shouted, much louder.

I wanted to hit my father, just then. "He gave the money away," I blurted out.

"What?"

"To the other performers at the zoo. The balloon artist, the one-armed juggler. The ones who don't make enough money on their own." I lowered my voice. "He said they needed the money more than you do."

My father glared down at me. He'd sweated through his shirt, and beads of perspiration limned the corners of his face. Behind him, two gray squirrels played cat-and-mouse along the roof of the neighbor's garage.

"How the fuck do you know that?"

"He told me," I said. I looked at the ground.

My father grabbed my shoulders, his fingers digging into my skin. He shook me hard. "Don't lie to me, kid."

"Okay, I saw him," I said.

My father's grip loosened slightly. I told him everything I wasn't supposed to tell: about our daily trips to the zoo, about how we spent the days with Simon, about how my stepmother did mime in the food court.

It was all over in seconds. When I was done, my father shoved me backwards against the stucco wall. "You'd make a lousy fucking spy, kid," he said. His eyes were smoldering.

He stormed up the back steps and slammed open the kitchen door.

"How long has this been going on?" he shouted.

"What's wrong?" I heard Sylvia ask.

"*You and the fucking mime!* The kid ratted on you."

"Please," begged my stepmother. "Simon will hear you."

"Who gives a shit if he hears me? He's the one who can't keep his cock to himself."

"Jesus Christ, Gary. It's not like that." And as far as I knew, it wasn't like that—at least not then. I watched their distorted outlines through the frosted kitchen window.

"The hell it's not! How stupid do you think I am?" I heard the sound of something shattering—maybe porcelain on tile. "If he doesn't leave tomorrow, I'll throw his shit into the street."

"You do that," shouted my stepmother, "I'm leaving."

After that, silence. I can still see them glaring at each other—at a total impasse, with nothing left to say. Then a door slammed. And another. When I finally sneaked back into the house around midnight, the lights were out and Sylvia was sleeping on the sofa.

My father—not Sylvia—picked me up from the community center the next day. He hadn't shaved and his halitosis was worse than usual. From his clothing, rumpled, improperly buttoned, rose a fetid stench of stale tobacco and unwashed bedding. "She says I don't communicate," he said. "Can you believe that shit? She's run off with a goddamn mime and *I* don't communicate." My father started the car before the passenger door was fully shut. On the drive to the city, we listened to Rush Limbaugh predicting the Sodom to come if Michael Dukakis ascended to the presidency.

"Do you remember where your idiot mother goes at the zoo?"

"No," I lied.

My father swerved around a slow-moving Cadillac. "Well, you'd better."

We found the zoo teeming with visitors. It was a warm, dry Friday afternoon—a rarity for the Bay Area in August—and people were making the most of it. The lines at the sno-cone stand extended past the koala cages; every seat on the carousel was occupied. The onlookers around the polar bear exhibit were so thick, you could hardly see through to the ice. When we arrived at the food court—my father periodically prodding my shoulder blades—it was standing-room only. My stepmother perched atop a wooden block at the foot of the mermaid-shaped fountain. Her pose was that of a sprinting deer. Around her milled teenage lovers, campers and counselors in matching T-shirts, a gaggle of overweight women enjoying ice cream. At the opposite end of the plaza, a larger crowd had gathered to watch Simon Stillman.

My father pushed through the crowd to Sylvia. She was barefoot. In front of her lay a naugahyde tote bag, brimming with cash. A cardboard sign beside the bag read: *Mime Over Matter: If You Don't Mime, It Matters.* Below that: *TIPS.* Near Sylvia's tiny left foot lay a small paper airplane.

"Would you get down from there?" called my father, breaking into the silence.

My stepmother held to her rigid pose.

The crowd opened up, shifting to include my father in the circle of spectators. Several parents looked at my disheveled father, then dragged away their young children. Others packed in to replace them. Few scenes draw spectators more quickly than a grown man antagonizing a mime.

"Enough of this bullshit," shouted my father. "Say something, dammit!"

My stepmother's gaze remained indifferent and fixed. More onlookers gravitated toward the action, maybe anticipating a show.

"Please, say something," said my father, his voice cracking ever so slightly. Then he softened his tone. "Please, Sylvia. Let's figure this out."

My father covered his eyes with his hand. For a moment, it appeared as though he might begin to cry. The crowd skulked backwards. This was personal now—dangerous. Far more than simply harassing a mime.

My stepmother remained silent and motionless. A lone grackle scavenged the asphalt beside her.

"Get the hell down from there, Sylvia," ordered my father, angry again. "You're making a goddamned fool of yourself." He raised his fist and shook it in the air, still shouting as the crowd retreated. I also inched away. Soon my father stood alone at the center of a growing circle, cursing, threatening, trapped behind the invisible walls of a no-mans-land that he'd created himself. ᛇ

Toledo, Ohio: 1967

Laurie Rosenblatt

When he is six Arcas asks his mother,
Where did I come from? She tells him, Family
and Child Services; shows him the photo of a baby
with crab-grass hair, impetigo, and the face
of an empty house. And when he's seven, the teacher
phones from school, Arcas paints entirely
in black and burps in class; sticks thumb tacks
into his arms. A cuckoo in the nest? Or fairy
child left in care of humans. Years later
he thinks, If 0 (unknown father) x 0
(absent mother) = Arcas: then I am Real.

෯

The Right Gift

Karin Lin-Greenberg

Ladybugs cover the ceiling of Graham's room like a roof of shiny red pushpins. Graham sees his grandmother, Louise, tilt her head back and look up; she clucks disapprovingly. Graham squints and looks up too. When he makes his vision fuzzy, the ladybugs are a solid block of red, as if someone took a paint roller and covered just the ceiling of the otherwise butter-colored room a bright crimson.

"My goodness," says Louise, "your room is covered in insects."

"Just the ceiling," says Graham. He always forgets how strong his grandmother's British accent is until she speaks. He doesn't understand how someone who has lived in America for sixty years could retain such a crisp accent. Graham has lived in Manhattan for all of his fifteen years, but he knows that if he moved to England his accent would adapt quickly.

The ladybugs have been in his room for three days now, and each night before going to bed, Graham picks several bugs out of his hair that have dropped from the ceiling. He runs the thin fingers of one hand through his shaggy chin-length black hair and cups the other to catch the ladybugs he has swept out. Then he lines the insects up on his index finger, lifts the window up two inches—as far as it will open—and blows them off his finger into the cool air outside.

"They've been here for a few days," says Graham, sitting up taller in the straight-backed brown plastic chair that has been provided for visitors. Graham is letting his grandmother use the wooden rocking chair that came with the room, although she has not yet sat down. He notices his grandmother looking down at his feet, at the sneakers she'd bought him last Christmas, which are now tattered, the soles separating from the uppers. She looks up, shakes her head, and sighs.

Today is the first day that Graham is allowed visitors; the doctors think it's best if patients aren't allowed visitors for the first two weeks so they can get used to life in the Health Center. Graham's parents aren't here today because they are in court, something to do with who gets what in the divorce, but Graham isn't surprised. They promised to come next weekend; his father on Saturday, his mother on Sunday.

It is strange, Graham thinks, to see his grandmother on a day that is not a holiday. At least on holidays there are other people to deflect attention. Graham is unsure whether he and his grandmother have ever had an entire conversation, just the two of them. He knows his grandmother is just trying to be nice and is only visiting because she feels bad for him.

She looks strange to Graham today, even though it's been only a few months since he last saw her—younger, healthier, skin tighter, as if she's had a face-lift. But, of course, she hasn't had any cosmetic surgery; that's the kind of thing Graham knows his grandmother considers frivolous. Maybe, thinks Graham, she only looks younger in comparison to the people who surround him here, young people with dry, pale skin and thinning hair, knobby knees and elbows, gray, old-looking teeth. They call this place The Health Center, which, Graham thinks, makes it seem deceptively happy, as if the place is filled with rosy-cheeked, shiny-eyed children brimming with health, instead of the skeletal teenagers struggling to keep a few spoonfuls of mush in their stomachs at each meal. Graham's heard that some of the other patients call it The Hell Center, which he thinks is not terribly original. He thinks it should be called The Bad Eater Academy or something along those lines.

"Well," says Louise, "we'll have to talk to someone about this infestation."

Infestation is such an ugly word. Graham has other words for the ladybugs: *a blanket of bugs* is his favorite. He imagines reaching up to the ceiling and grabbing a corner of the ladybug blanket; the rest of the blanket will follow and float down to his bed in a smooth, cool sheet. He'll cover his body and disappear in a sea of red.

Every day the patients, or guests as they are called, are each allowed half an hour on the computer. After the ladybugs appeared, Graham searched the Internet and read about a legend that killing a ladybug would cause bad luck and sickness. Graham isn't sure if he believes in legends, but he doesn't want to test this one out, so he refuses to allow the exterminator in his room.

"Oh!" exclaims Louise, as a ladybug swivels down from the ceiling and flies into her forehead. She swipes at the air in front of her face, even though the ladybug is long gone, has disappeared into the room somewhere.

Graham has been obsessed with the ladybugs. They are the most entertainment he's had in the last two weeks. He finds the other patients dull and tedious, even though he probably seems dull and tedious in the same way. When he looks at the other patients, he is constantly reminded of what is wrong with him and thinks he'd do better out in the real world. But his father insisted on this six-week stay at The Health Center, as if six weeks will fix everything.

Every once in a while a ladybug will drop from the ceiling, wings working in circles like a propeller. When the ladybugs let loose, Graham pretends that he is in a video game, that he is the target and the ladybugs are aiming for him. He ducks and twists, but without fail, some hit him. If no one is around, Graham makes exploding sounds, as if the ladybugs have caused him to detonate. After he is hit three times, Graham makes the "Game Over" sound, the old video arcade "Wah wah wah," descending an octave.

"I'll speak to someone immediately and get you moved," Louise says, as another ladybug flies near her face. "It doesn't make sense to have your father pay all this money for a room filled with insects."

"The people here know about them," Graham says. "They've moved everyone else with ladybugs into another wing, but I don't want to move."

"That is just silly," says Louise, and Graham shrugs. He is, in fact, tired of this room, tired of Monet's water lilies hanging on one yellow wall and Van Gogh's sunflowers hanging on the other. It reminds Graham of a bank. If he's moved, he'll only end up in another room with the same prints on the walls, the same yellow paint. The only good part about this room is the ladybugs.

"Do you think they're blind?" says Graham.

"Who?"

"The ladybugs. They just fly into things. Like they can't see at all."

"I have no idea," says Louise, looking at the ceiling and shaking her head. "I'd really like to speak to someone about them. I wonder if they carry diseases."

"They don't."

"How do you know?"

"Because people like them. People always kill bugs they think are bad, but they don't usually kill ladybugs."

"Regardless, you should get a new room. I'll find someone to speak with now. These things," says Louise, sweeping her hand toward the ceiling, "need to be exterminated."

"No. I'm not moving." His grandmother's use of the word "exterminated" makes his skin crawl, as if the ladybugs have covered his body and are skittering along his flesh. The word seems unnecessarily cruel.

Louise sighs. "You're always so stubborn. You never listen when people try to tell you what's good for you." She looks as if she's about to say more, but stops herself and spends a few moments rearranging her tweed skirt.

Graham's father always calls Louise stubborn, says she can't adapt to the world around her. Whenever they see each other, they end up yelling and screaming in disapproval of the other. Graham doesn't want to argue with his grandmother, knows it will get him nowhere, so he says, "Is it true that ladybugs are called ladybirds in England?" This is one of the facts he learned while doing his Internet research.

Louise nods.

They are silent for a moment, then Louise looks at the ceiling again. "I'll call your father tonight. Let him know about the infestation. Then he can decide what to do."

Graham isn't listening to his grandmother now. Instead, he is looking out the window. The leaves are turning red on the trees outside. He wonders whether there will be snow on the ground by the time he gets out.

Louise opens her large black purse, rummages inside and pulls out a package wrapped in gold paper. She places it in Graham's lap, then sits in the rocking chair across from him. Suddenly, Graham notices how small his grandmother is; her feet don't touch the ground. As she rocks back and forth, she barely lands on her toes. Graham now feels guilty, as if he is a small child and this gift is to appease him because he's finally stopped fussing. But then he realizes that it is a sympathy gift. People don't just bring presents on days that are not Christmas or birthdays.

"This will give you something to do," says Louise. "Something to keep you busy until you get out."

Graham picks up the package and tries to guess what is inside by the weight. It is a small box and he thinks it must contain something dull, like dominoes or a pack of playing cards with a book of card games.

Graham notices that Louise is looking at him with anticipation. Whatever the gift is, he'll have to pretend it is the best thing in the world, pretend it's something that he's always wanted. Graham looks down at the present and can tell that the paper has been used before, recycled from some other gift. He slips his fingernail under the tape to lift it carefully away from the paper. He knows his grandmother will be pleased that the wrapping can be used yet again. He's sure that she has single-handedly saved hundreds of trees in her lifetime.

It is a Game Boy Advance, an absolutely perfect present for a fifteen-year-old boy. Graham stares at the box in his hands. He is stunned at its perfection, and runs his fingers along the slick, plastic-wrapped edges of the unopened box. His grandmother has always been generous with him, but her generosity is usually tinged with practicality.

Since he started running at the age of seven, she'd bought him a new pair of sneakers for Christmas and another for his birthday in the summer every year. He usually wore through a pair of running shoes in three months and had to get another pair, but he never told his grandmother this, always pretending that she was the only one who ever bought him sneakers.

"Don't you like it?" says Louise, and Graham looks up.

He realizes that he hasn't spoken since he unwrapped the present. How did his grandmother even know about video games? How did she know that he loves to play them, that he's missed the games he spent so much time playing at home in front of the TV? How could she have known that he wanted to ask his father for a video game, but he just felt too guilty to ask for anything?

Graham still holds the box in his hands, silent. The sneakers were easy to receive: try them on, roll from the ball of the foot to the heel, announce they fit perfectly. But of course they would; he'd clip a picture of the sneakers he wanted from the shoe review section of *Runner's World*, write his size in the margin in black marker. Later, when he won races—and he would always win because he was the best, the fastest—he'd cut articles from his school newspaper and the local paper and send them to his grandmother. Then she would tape these articles to her refrigerator. The cycle would continue with new sneakers every six months, but now this gift seems an acknowledgement that things have changed, that there will be no more running, at least for a while. This video game, although perfect, seems a betrayal.

"Well," says Louise, "don't you like it? The salesboy said it's what all young men like nowadays."

Graham tries to will himself to say thank you, but instead he snaps back with, "I won't be here forever, you know." He does not know where the sudden anger came from. Maybe it's about the shoes. Maybe it's about the ladybugs. Graham doesn't know.

His grandmother looks shocked, and Graham wishes he could just say thank you, just make his mouth form the words, but he can't. He sets the game down on the nightstand beside his bed, folds his arms across his chest, and tries to will away tears.

"No," says Louise, shaking her head, "let's hope you won't be in here forever."

Graham desperately wants to say thank you, wants to tell her that she's done a good job, but he can't speak. He sits quietly, stares at the box in his hands, and doesn't blink until a ladybug drops onto the box and skids off the edge of the smooth plastic into his lap.

Louise wants to feed her family. It is March of 1940, and Louise is twenty-two and lives in London with her husband and two young sons. Her husband has found work in a factory that manufactures parts for military planes, and finally there is some money coming in. But the country is at war, and everyone must be cautious; food is carefully rationed. Louise knows how much food each member of her family is allotted, knows these numbers as well as she knew her multiplication tables while she was in school. Four ounces of bacon or ham per person, twelve ounces of sugar, four ounces of butter. Three-and-a-half pints of milk for each of her boys. Although there is not enough money for another child, Louise almost wishes she were expecting; pregnant women are allowed seven pints of milk a week and up to eighteen eggs per month. She could give those eggs to her boys, help them grow tall and strong.

Louise's life seems to be wholly about stretching a little to make, if not a lot, more. She is whisking butter into warm milk, which she will leave to set and then, even though the butter will not be as rich, it will be more. She wonders if her work is harder than her husband's, and thinks it is. She is expected to perform miracles in the kitchen, to feed her hungry husband and two growing boys. This is the modern-day equivalent of weaving straw into gold and she jokingly refers to her kitchen as the alchemy laboratory. Her husband smiles when she says this, but she can see sadness beneath the smile, can tell he wishes he could come home with a twenty-pound bag of sugar, wishes that his boys could spread thick layers of smooth butter upon freshly-baked bread. Doing without is practiced conscientiously, becomes ingrained. Louise feels as though it is almost a religion. Yet she smiles through it all, keeps stretching, trades recipes with her neighbors because, after all, what else can she do?

Graham wants to be thin. It is September of 2004 and Graham lives on the Upper West side of Manhattan with only his mother now, since his father moved out six months ago.

Thin. He loves the word itself—slim, concise, four letters. He is studying Spanish in school and the Spanish word for thin is "flaco," two syllables, too much. Even worse is "delgado," three syllables. Words should sound like their meanings.

Graham knows that he is getting thinner, but still it isn't enough. He wants to be the thinnest and the fastest, wants to propel his body so quickly that he is a flash, wants people to wonder whether they even saw someone racing past them.

He wakes at 5 a.m. to run in Riverside Park before coming home for breakfast, which is a packet of Sweet and Low, sprinkled on two saltine crackers. Graham likes the explosion of salt against sweetness in his mouth. Until his father left, his parents were always arguing by the time he returned, and no one noticed what he ate for months; no one noticed anything until he collapsed in school and the ambulance had to rush him away.

Since his father left, his mother sleeps later, is still asleep when he leaves for school. Graham skips breakfast sometimes, spends lunchtime in the school library; no one really misses him at lunch. He spends most of his time alone, and is hardly noticed. He only gets attention when he wins trophies for the school's track team. Otherwise, he is nearly invisible.

Some days when he comes home, his mother has left him a chicken breast or a steak defrosting on the counter. She works late and Graham always tells her that he's already eaten when she comes home. But really he takes the meat to the garbage chute, and sends it tumbling down, listening as the icy sides clank against metal. Then he wipes off the moist counter with a paper towel and takes out his secret stash of condiment packets, stored in a shoebox under his bed.

Graham likes packets: sugar, ketchup, mustard, honey. Packets mean control, a precise allotment. Graham knows the calorie counts of most foods as well as he knows the statistics for his favorite track stars.

After he eats something small and controlled, Graham will go for another run, longer and more punishing than the last; he will run until his body will not go anymore. He feels he has no choice but to run until every inch of his body sears with pain.

Louise has handed Graham a present, and he is unwrapping it slowly and carefully. She looks at her grandson, thin and pale, and thinks he seems either like a very old man or a newborn baby, but she can't decide which. When her son Simon called and said in a grave voice that Graham was sick, her heart dropped, assuming cancer. She had a brother who'd died of leukemia in childhood, and she remembers watching his miserable wasting away. When Simon said Graham's diagnosis was anorexia and exercise addiction, Louise was baffled. Now her grandson looks more like this long-dead brother than she cares to admit, and it makes her feel sad and angry and helpless.

As Graham slowly opens the gift, Louise lets her eyes drift up to the ceiling again. She is troubled by the insects that fill her grandson's room. She wonders whether they carry disease, whether they will harm her grandson. He already looks so delicate that she doesn't want anything else to hurt him. She tries to count the ladybirds on the ceiling, but there are too many. There are hundreds of the tiny red insects, and her eyesight begins to blur as she examines them. This room, she thinks, is filled with things she does not understand: why would these insects prefer to be indoors, hunched together on the ceiling of this room? Why would her grandson starve himself, push his body to such extremes? For a moment, Louise feels dizzy, overwhelmed by all that she does not understand.

"Well," says Louise, "don't you like it? The salesboy said it's what all young men like nowadays."

When she went to the store to pick up a gift, Louise couldn't tell the salesman the truth, couldn't explain this strange, unfathomable disease that her grandson, a child who seemingly had everything, had inflicted upon himself. She wanted to confide in the fat, oily-skinned salesboy, who suddenly seemed to embody what a healthy American boy should be, but instead she surprised herself with the lie that flowed from her lips. She told the salesboy that her grandson was a football player, added American football, in case he wasn't picturing hulking boys in padded uniforms, said he'd broken his leg—a terrible fracture, she said—when he was tackled. He'd be in the hospital recovering for a few weeks, she said, adding that there would be lots of physical therapy. The salesboy recommended the Game Boy, which Louise thought looked no bigger than a calculator and wondered how it could provide hours of entertainment. But she didn't even look at the price, simply nodded and handed the boy her credit card; she wanted to get out of the store and away from her lie as quickly as possible.

Graham still has not said thank you, but looks up at Louise with tired eyes and snaps, "I won't be in here forever, you know."

Louise is shocked, unsure what to make of this statement. There is so much hostility behind her grandson's words. She'd never said anything about his being here forever. She only bought him the game as something to occupy his time, something to keep his hands busy.

"No," Louise says, shaking her head, "let's hope you won't be in here forever." She'd gotten curious, simply had to know how much it cost to keep the boy here, and looked up the price of Graham's stay. She was shocked to see that six weeks here would cost more than the most lavish vacation she could dream up. She was angry at herself for needing to know the cost, angry again for actually finding out, then she was angry at this place for charging so much. Finally, she was angry with her son for spending such a grotesque amount of money; he'd never known the value of a dollar. She'd always saved and budgeted, first in London, then in New York, where she'd worked as a third grade teacher for thirty years. Her sons, both in business, made money too fast, too easily, never understood value, had forgotten the difficult early years.

Louise came here because she wanted to see her grandson, but she also wanted to see this place, this Health Center. She wasn't sure what she'd been expecting, perhaps rooms that replicated the finest hotel suites in the world, but instead she found a dull, antiseptic room filled with insects. This is not what she'd anticipated. And now there is Graham's stubborn refusal to be moved from the room.

Graham has put the game on the nightstand beside his bed and it reminds Louise of a quickly discarded Christmas present, something unappealing to the recipient. She'd been sure that Graham would like the gift; the salesboy had seemed so certain it was the right thing. Now Louise feels the guilt she experiences when she chooses a restaurant for a group dinner and the food is poorly prepared. She always feels guilty, as if she'd cooked everything herself. And now she's feeling the same way, that something awful has happened but she has no power over it.

"Do you already have one of these?" asks Louise, pointing to the game, and Graham shakes his head.

"No. No. It's not that." He is choked up and can barely speak. He looks as if he is trying to hold back tears. Louise wishes she could understand, wishes she could fix this, somehow patch things up. She is not sure what she has done wrong, whether he's crying over her or something else. For all she knows, he could be crying over the impending extermination of the insects in his room.

Finally, Graham chokes out, "Thank you," but Louise isn't sure what to read into the statement. It sounds forced, as if her grandson has just learned to speak, laboring over each word.

"Well, you're welcome," says Louise. "I suppose." They are sitting in chairs directly across from each other, and there is nothing to do but look out the window. "The leaves are pretty," says Louise, and Graham nods. He still looks as if he will cry.

As she rocks back and forth in a rocking chair, Louise lets her eyes wander to her grandson's legs. They look so thin now through the cloth of his khaki pants. His knees are too big for his bony legs, and they remind her of her husband's, before he died ten years ago. These are not the legs of a young man, especially one who used to be such a strong runner.

Louise always admired Graham's running, respected the boy's dedication. Running was a sport that made sense to her, something simple and elegant and beautiful. It wasn't a clunky sport, like hockey, which required so much gear that the player nearly disappeared beneath the padding. Running was a sport that needed only a pair of shoes and a strong will; a sport molded out of nothing. Louise has bought Graham running shoes twice a year for as long as she can remember, shoes that led her grandson to victory after victory. But now, she wonders, will he be strong enough to run again?

And suddenly it dawns on her. Graham must have expected a new pair of running shoes. She can hardly remember ever giving him anything else. Surely there must have been stuffed animals and rattles when he was younger, but for most of his life, they'd measured the years with two pairs of running shoes, one on his birthday and another pair at Christmas. Like her, Graham is a creature of habit. Louise realizes that she has knocked off the simple balance between them, and she must restore it.

Graham turns his head to Louise and attempts a smile. "Thank you for coming," he says. Louise smiles back and nods. She isn't sure whether she is being dismissed, told that she can go home now, since they seem to have nothing more to say to each other. But perhaps he truly is thankful, glad that someone is here with him.

"I'll come again," Louise says. "I'll come with your father next weekend." It will be better then, thinks Louise. There will be more people around, more ways to deflect the awkward silences. She will right things when she brings him the running shoes.

"But don't call him about the ladybugs, okay? Let's just leave them here for a while," says Graham.

The insects again, thinks Louise, but she nods, gives in to his wishes. She looks up again at the ceiling. She concedes that they are rather beautiful, odd and perhaps not completely unwelcome guests. Several minutes ago the first ladybird fell from the ceiling and startled her, but now she has watched more fall gracefully through the air. When their wings move, they look almost golden; Louise thinks that if she squints they would look like shooting stars falling through her grandson's room.

Louise suddenly remembers a piece of folk wisdom she'd read in a very old book when she was a young girl: if a ladybird lands on a sick person, it will take the sickness away with it when it flies off. If this is true, she wants all the bugs to drop from the ceiling onto her grandson's body, coat him—the way she's seen bees cover beekeepers' bodies in documentaries about harvesting honey—then fly away, a red swirl of insects, flowing like smoke out the window.

"Okay," says Louise. "We'll leave the ladybirds for now. Let them keep you company."

"Thank you," says Graham, and this time he sounds genuine.

Louise stands, tells Graham that she will go, but she'll be back next week. As Louise hugs Graham, she notices a ladybird in his hair, and she resists the urge to run her fingers through the strands and pluck it out. She hopes the ladybird will fly away on its own, that it will take away Graham's sickness, that it will make things better, that it will do what she can't. And then, as she kisses Graham's dry cheek, she chastises herself, tells herself that she is being silly, that wishing on insects is preposterous. But what else can she do?

She moves near the bed and surreptitiously slides the game across the nightstand, lets it slip into her large purse. She will return it, so it will not cause Graham to cry anymore. She'll buy a new pair of running shoes—size ten, she remembers from the summer—and she'll bring them next time, the right gift. &

Twenty Years Later, My Sister is Still Drowning

Kelli Russell Agodon

She tells me about the ovenbird, its orange crown traveling swamps after sunset. She says it keeps an infant under its wing, tells me birds can sense children underwater. The dishes soaked overnight and though she knows it's just her reflection between suds, she mentions Jude, how saints appear in the waves of every body of water. We never talk about her second summer when she disappeared into the lake, the kingfisher hovering above her, the water that entered and exited in a burst as our father tossed her to shore shouting, *Breathe, breathe!* When she opens the refrigerator she laughs as she sees the cantaloupe. *Someone has carved God into the orange center,* she says as if this world has not flooded around us, as if everything she said made sense.

৪০

Consultation

Erika Dreifus

Kleptomania wasn't really the issue. That much, Len Eisenberg understood. It was the end of the day and Len sat in his office, listening to Doug Stevenson on the other end of the telephone.

"To a degree, that *is* the issue," insisted Doug, his friend and colleague since medical school, twenty years ago.

"That's why this patient was sent to me in the first place," Doug went on. "That was part of the deal."

Len reached for the *Diagnostic and Statistical Manual* and thumbed through until he found the criteria for "312.32 Kleptomania." He hadn't encountered this disorder in years: "*Recurrent failure to resist impulses to steal objects that are not needed for personal use or for their monetary value...Increasing sense of tension immediately before committing the theft...Pleasure, gratification, or relief at the time of committing the theft.*" And so on.

Len closed the book and set it on his desk. "Plea bargain?"

"No, the jury actually convicted her."

She had been coming to Doug's office for five months, Doug explained to Len, during the Tuesday/Thursday 4PM slot. Although the work had started slowly ("quite a lot of resistance," Doug said) they had, in fact, established a healthy therapeutic alliance and begun to acquire some insight into her lack of impulse control.

Until that Tuesday, just about six weeks ago.

Charlotte, whose office was just a few feet from Doug's, had begun seeing a new patient Tuesdays and Thursdays at 3:30PM. Thus the trouble commenced.

"But why?" Len asked. Doug had taken him on a quick tour of the set-up after the renovations, and Len had been impressed. One office to the left, one to the right. A cheery waiting room into which Doug or Charlotte, depending on the time, would emerge to greet each patient; no signs on the door to indicate the names of the therapists. And it was all connected to their house. Len, on the other hand, maintained his practice in a medical building across town. His wife, Susan, hadn't been so enthusiastic about having his patients quite so close to home.

"The patients don't even see each other in that waiting room, since you have them coming in at different times, right?" Len continued. "I always thought that staggered system worked so well, to avoid having them sitting in the waiting room together."

Until *that* Tuesday, Doug had agreed. "Now I just wish the two of them, the patients, could work this out on their own."

Len said nothing for a moment. "I still don't quite understand. How does the kleptomania fit in?"

"Charlotte's three-thirty leaves a backpack in the waiting room, and an *open* backpack—I mean, unzipped, literally open, practically inviting my patient to go fishing when she arrives for her appointments just before four. If we weren't dealing with kleptomania, the timing wouldn't be a problem."

It was true that the reasons why Charlotte's patient had to "leave his mark," so to speak (it was a "him," Doug confirmed) in the waiting room formed another set of challenging questions. But Doug had telephoned Len because this habit of leaving the backpack had wrought profound, if not dire, consequences for Doug's patient. Threatened the therapeutic alliance. Ergo, the need for consultation.

"Tell me about her," Len said, as he found a pen and paper.

The woman had begun stealing about seven years earlier, Doug explained, and was now in her late twenties. She was married ("most of them are," he noted) but had no children. She had presented with a history of trichotillomania, but that was over; the eyelashes had all grown back. Nor were material needs the issue; she was descended from an old New England family whose name was discreetly carved into the walls of many local hospitals, museums, and colleges (Doug named a few). She had married her boarding-school sweetheart; she lived in the city but maintained a horse at a stable somewhere (in fact, initially she'd stated that her only requirement for therapy was that her sessions not conflict with her riding schedule). No material reason could possibly compel her to waltz in and out of drugstores to steal travel-size containers of shampoo and shaving cream and Sudafed.

"Travel-size?" Len shifted the phone and jotted some notes.

"She loves packing and unpacking. Traces of the obsessive-compulsive. The backpack doesn't help."

"I see," Len said.

They laughed in unison. As residents, they'd practiced those "I see's" together.

"So you'll take the consult?" Doug asked. "I know I can help her, if we can just get through this impasse. She keeps threatening to quit if I don't intervene with the other therapist and 'do something.'" Again Doug paused. "Len, you've been terrific, before. I'm thinking of—well, I'm sure you know which case I'm thinking of."

Len knew. "Ms. H." Or so he would have called her if he'd had the wherewithal to convince Doug to work on writing up that case with him. But maybe he would have had to choose another initial. You were supposed to disguise patients as much as possible when you wrote about them. Doug knew all about that. Unlike Len, he was prolific in the literature of their field, and already had two books to his credit, in addition to dozens of journal articles and reviews.

Len looked at his appointment book. His own practice was thriving, as his wife kept pointing out, and these days he was trying to get home by 7, this last year before Amanda went off to college and left Susan and him alone in a very empty nest.

"Len?" Doug said. "I could really use your help."

Was that a tinge of desperation in Doug's voice? "Doug...have you talked to Charlotte about this?"

His friend and colleague sighed. "You know how she can be."

Yes. Len knew how she could be. He'd also known Dr. Charlotte Cowles since medical school. Sometimes he still felt embarrassed about this history, his very obvious crush on her back then, how he'd stammered his way through asking her out to dinner long before she and Doug had even become a couple. And though he wouldn't admit it to anyone, he wondered if Doug and Charlotte still thought about that episode from their common past, or talked about it, or even laughed about it. About him.

"So," Doug was saying. "You and I will talk again—after the consultation."

Len closed the book. "Sure. Have the patient call me."

This would be an interesting case.

So interesting, Len sensed, that even before the patient telephoned and left a message and he'd called her back and arranged a meeting, he'd given her a name—Mrs. K. Because right after that conversation with Doug, he had started thinking. It was one thing to have his hours filled. He took pride in that, and in having reached a point where, as Susan repeatedly observed whenever he admitted a sense of professional inadequacy to her, his colleagues referred new patients and consults to him. But he wanted to do more, professionally. He wanted some public credit, dammit, and that didn't come easy in this business. Maybe Doug's patient would become the subject of a case study he could write up. With Doug. Or maybe—even better—he and Doug could present it together at the Institute. Everyone at the Institute liked Doug. Imagine what it could mean for him, Len, to collaborate publicly with Dr. Stevenson, whom everyone acknowledged would be the Institute's President in the not too distant future.

"Mrs. K arrived promptly for the initial meeting with the consulting psychiatrist," he could begin his section of the work. He wouldn't, of course, include the equally true details: that she wore tan slacks and a black sweater with a scarf knotted around her neck; that the diamond on her hand was large, but not garish; that her fingernails were perfectly shaped and coated in a clear polish. On the other hand, it was noteworthy that, for someone with a history of obsessive-compulsive disorder, she sat remarkably still, no foot-tapping or knuckle-cracking, and certainly no hair-pulling; she met his gaze fairly steadily, as well.

"So, Dr. Eisenberg," she said. "I suppose you know why I'm here."

"I'd like you to tell me," Len said.

She folded her hands. "I suppose you could say that I'm here to pay a shrink I don't know $175 to tell him about the problems I'm having with the shrink I do know. That's the deal, right?"

Len kept his tone even. "You have come for a consultation with me, and, as with all my consultations, I charge a fee for my time and services." In a way, she'd done him a favor, raising the money issue so early. "The question is: what has led to this consultation, and how might this session be helpful to you?"

"That's two questions."

He waited. Ten seconds. Fifteen.

Of course, she started to talk. She said that Doug (naturally, she called him "Dr. Stevenson") was a very nice man. She had nothing against him, personally. But she felt that if he sincerely wanted to further her treatment, he would say something to the other therapist in the office, whoever that person was, about that other patient who so thoughtlessly left his or her "stuff" out there, wide open no less, in the waiting room.

"I mean, anyone could just walk in off the street and steal something. Keys, wallet." She laughed. "I mean, someone who really *needs* the money." She gazed at the wall and her expression darkened. "*I* would only take a little bottle of whatever. Tylenol. Or a pack of tissues. That would be enough for me. But it would serve whoever it is right. Who would just leave their stuff out there, like that? '*Invitation au voyage*.'"

Silence, for more than ten seconds.

Len knew that Baudelaire poem. His wife, who taught high school English and World Literature, read French poetry aloud from time to time. Usually this irritated him, reminding him how little they shared professionally. But now he was grateful for Susan's unintended assistance.

She loves packing and unpacking, Doug had said to him. He imagined Mrs. K astride her horse. He wanted to ask if the horse was named Baudelaire. But all he said was: "Something stopped you."

She stared. "Do you guys *practice* those lines, or what?"

He worked to keep his face unmoving. "You sound very angry."

She exhaled. She began to drum her fingers against the chair's arm.

"Do you want to talk about why you're so angry? Or with whom?" he said evenly.

Another breath.

"Maybe we should talk a bit more about *exactly* why you're here," he suggested. Then he explained that as consultant, he had heard only a minimum from her therapist about the current difficulties. It was his job now to hear her perspective on what had "gotten in the way" of the therapeutic alliance between her and Dr. Stevenson. He didn't use that precise term ("therapeutic alliance") because they had learned in residency that one should avoid it with patients. He said instead to Mrs. K, "rapport." He would then work with Dr. Stevenson, he explained, to help determine the best strategy to restore that working relationship so that her treatment could proceed.

"Does that make sense?" he said. "We'll talk today, and—" He noticed she was holding her breath, watching him. "And if we think it will be helpful, we'll meet perhaps one more time."

What Mrs. K didn't realize, but Len, of course, knew very well, was that "the other therapist in the office"— whose magazines, had Mrs. K ever bothered to peruse them, bore address labels marked *Dr. Charlotte Cowles*; whose patient (or whose patient's backpack) had so profoundly threatened not merely the complete success, but the utter viability, of Mrs. K's treatment; whose presence, Len was acutely aware, even if Mrs. K was not, was just as much, if not perhaps more, in demand on the professional conference and journal board circuit as Dr. Stevenson's—the other therapist was none other than *Mrs.* Dr. Stevenson.

Further, there were tensions, Len knew, that already existed in the marital relationship (thanks to the generous provisions of Veuve-Clicquot at the Institute's last Holiday Party, and Doug's fondness for fine champagne), many of which concerned the couple's real-life offspring. Charlotte believed that Doug tended to be excessively protective of their fifteen-year-old daughter, that he needed to resolve some extraordinarily deep conflicts over her emerging sexuality. Doug had countered that Charlotte was engaged in a sadistic re-enactment of her own adolescent relationship with her own mother. These conversations, Doug had told Len, tended to combust into verbal conflagrations that their daughter, Julia, and her twelve-year old brother, Jonathan, might or might not have overheard, Doug acknowledged, when Len had asked. Given these significant tensions, it was, therefore, quite evident to Len as well as to Doug that approaching Charlotte to discuss this situation involving their respective patients—who, it did not take Sigmund Freud to recognize, served as repositories of the therapists' own desires for success and achievement and also, for better or for worse, represented, for this pair of married therapists, their own children—was a step to be taken carefully, if at all.

"Why don't I just come here and see *you*, from now on?" Mrs. K asked at their second meeting, stretching a black-stockinged ankle, turning it.

Len kept his gaze fixed on her face. "Can you say more about that?" She still hadn't indicated whether she even realized that "the other therapist" was a woman, let alone someone intimately involved with Dr. Stevenson, with whom, Len was convinced, Mrs. K surely had begun to enter the throes of transference love. There was more to this backpack business than the kleptomania. He was sure of it. He just wanted her to realize this herself. He wanted her to see that the backpack served as a tangible reminder that it wasn't just the two of them, Dr. Stevenson and herself, alone in that office suite. That no matter what fantasies might be simmering beneath the surface (consciously or unconsciously), Mrs. K truly did not occupy very much space in Dr. Stevenson's life—even if those Tuesday and Thursday appointments might be growing ever more essential to hers.

She smiled. "Well, *you* don't share an office with anyone. It would just be easier to come here instead of going to Dr. Stevenson's. And we seem to get along quite well, you and me." The smile broadened, invitingly.

This happened, not altogether infrequently, when he was called to consult. It had, for example, occurred with that Ms. H case. Not exactly a divide and conquer situation, not even a replica of playing one parent off another. More elusive, more layered than that.

He began the familiar explanation now, about how that wasn't the point of the consultation, how likely it was that whatever issues had truly led to the impasse with Dr. Stevenson would arise with him as well.

"I don't think so," she said. The smile disappeared. "I think *you* really have my best interests at heart."

She was good. She was very, very good.

Or she was very, very miserable.

After twenty years in this job, shouldn't he know the difference?

Charlotte refused to "disrupt" her own patient's treatment, Doug reported to Len the following week. The young man had issues, she said, with feeling that he was entitled to occupy any space at all, anywhere. With feeling safe. If she were even to intimate to him that he couldn't trust the space of her waiting room…

"*Your* waiting room?" Doug had rejoined.

"*Our* waiting room, *our* waiting room!" she had practically screamed. "For Christ's sake, Doug! The guy has no idea you exist!"

"Is that true?" In truth, Len had always been fascinated by the dynamics of the marriages of therapist couples who shared work space. What images and fantasies their patients reported about their "colleagues." How one dealt with that.

"Probably. Who cares?" Doug said now. "You should hear what some of my patients say about Charlotte, the ones who have seen her around the office. Not exactly complimentary."

"Really?" As far as Len was concerned—and this opinion had not changed despite Charlotte's rejection back in medical school—there was very little about Charlotte Cowles not to be complimentary about.

"Yes, but—we're getting off track, here. The point is that my charming wife refuses to help. And you know, it isn't the first time." For a moment it seemed that he was about to say more about Charlotte, and Len waited. But then it was back to business. "So it's up to us to solve this, to help this woman on our own."

"Absolutely," Len agreed, jotting more notes in the little book he'd now given over to this case.

He didn't have another meeting scheduled with Mrs. K, but the case was still on his mind. He kept thinking of potential solutions and strategies, to discuss with Doug. The ideal, of course, would be to have Mrs. K work through both the impasse and the impulse control issues. What an incredibly successful outcome that would be. Definitely one for the books. Indeed. Forget Anna O. Forget Dora. Mrs. K…Mrs. K….

Two more weeks passed, and again it was the end of the day, but it was also the end of the week. Len picked up the phone and pushed the buttons for his voice-mail messages. The usual weekend separation anxiety from the depressive he'd seen three hours earlier. A call from his mother. Susan, reminding him to call his mother. And then another female voice. He found himself ashamed—but not altogether surprised—by the pleasure he experienced in hearing that particular inflection.

But why had Charlotte Cowles called? And addressed him not as "Len," but as "Dr. Eisenberg?"

"So, I'm sorry to be bothering you," she had said, into the mailbox.

That was unlike Charlotte. She'd always been rather dismissive of him, in fact, even back when they were younger, especially after he'd dared ask her to dinner, that second year of medical school. And professionally, he probably heard from Doug fifty times for every time Charlotte called.

"But I'm really worried about my parents," the message continued.

And then it dawned on him. It wasn't Charlotte. It was Julia. Doug and Charlotte's daughter.

"And I don't know exactly how, but I know you're involved," the girl's voice continued. "I've heard them mention your name. I really need to talk with you."

What was that joke a supervisor had told him, way back? *You know what the child of a psychiatrist wants to be when he grows up?* Len had waited. The supervisor smiled. *A patient.*

He was tempted to find out just what Julia Stevenson was thinking. But what if the roles were reversed? If his daughter had called Doug? What if Doug had then, without informing him, gone ahead and met with Amanda, especially, Len reminded himself, when she was only fifteen?

"So she must have overheard something," Doug said, when he returned Len's message. "But I don't know how. We're usually very careful about that." He was silent for a long moment, and Len couldn't help wondering just how many arguments, how much screaming actually took place when these therapists weren't with their patients.

"I'd be happy to meet with her," Len offered, quickly.

"No, we'll handle it," Doug said firmly. "Thank you."

They handled it.

Or at least, Len assumed that they did. Doug didn't mention the matter again. And he didn't send Mrs. K back either.

"I'm handling that, too," Doug said, when Len asked, at the next Institute party a couple of months later. "Charlotte's come around, a bit. Who knows?" He laughed, and much as Len tried, there seemed no way to detect how much force lay beneath the heartiness. "Maybe she and I will write this whole thing up sometime." Doug set down his glass next to the crudités and touched Len's shoulder. "Maybe we'll even ask you to look it over. You weren't exactly uninvolved here, you know." He winked, then walked away, toward the woman standing across the room, the woman so deserving of compliments, whose eyes, Len saw, had just met Doug's and surely were, Len surmised, the cause of the smile now covering Doug's face.

Len stood there, stunned. His heart pounded against the notebook weighty in his jacket pocket, the notebook that he'd given over to the Mrs. K case. He was jolted back only when he heard another voice.

"It's like they're on a second honeymoon," another therapist was commenting to a colleague as she plucked a carrot from the plate. She eyed Doug and Charlotte. "Everyone's noticed it."

Len took a breath, then pressed his lips together. It was time to move from the crudités to the bar.

His own practice was thriving, he reminded himself. That's what his wife said. And he wanted to spend more time at home these days before Amanda went off to college, anyway. And if he never published books or received the public recognition that he wanted, that he deserved—well, he would have to learn to make peace with that somehow, too.

Of course, he still believed Mrs. K's was an interesting case. And if anyone asked, he could still say a lot about it. Because kleptomania wasn't really the issue. That much, Len Eisenberg understood. ❧

Psychotherapist at the Landfill

Lou Lipsitz

> —*for Bob Phillips*

1—
On an early morning in my seventy-first year
    it is a mixed thing
    to come to the county landfill
and in the piercing yellow light inter
these scribbled notes of bewilderment,
attentiveness and odd, interminable hope.

To bury them among garbage heaps
and old appliances: one hundred twenty-two
boxes of records, manila folders
filled with my writing—
    forty years of dreams taken down
    forty years of dilemmas,
    visitations from the archetypal powers,
forty years of human beings
talking out loud to themselves and to me,
pages, an unbelievable accumulation now;
evidence of how we humans struggle and ruminate,
trying against so much training,
so much fear, to dig
through the long, heavy dark and raise the dead—
    accomplish the slow, uncertain resurrection
    of becoming ourselves.

Because I could not bear to have them shredded
I now carry the boxes out
amidst the debris and dust of the landfill
and lay them here thinking somehow
they will be left alone to decay and vanish
in their own time, decompose under the stars.

Only I am wrong.
The bulldozer appears so quickly;
snorting and shoving things aside

burying the pile in efficient sweeps of its yellow plow.
    Then they're gone, pushed under—
    the fine attunements, the record of all
    I was able to make sense from—
gone into the garbage
—forty years worth in forty seconds.
Instant burial!

2—
And then for a week
    I can't sleep in peace.
    I wake every morning
    and know something is wrong, unfinished.

And finally, I grasp it and go back.
I have the smudge stick with me this time
and the sage and fragrant cedar.
This time, I go up to the bulldozer,
silent, unattended now, and mark it
with my stick.
    This time, I create the fire
    and speak my makeshift
    native american/modern man
prayer:
    Commit these writings, these
    scribblings half understood, memories
    of spirit struggles, to the Great Mystery.
    May they find their place,
    a breath of our strange journey,
    often obscure to us, that nonetheless,
    we yearn to know.

The smoke rises and I think of the road
I have taken myself: seventy now,
retired detective of dreams.
A mixed thing to be here with prayers and endings.
My soul feels its damp exhausted
exhilaration—
    letting go of all that was healed
    and not healed—
my long initiation through the comradely, lonely,
stinging sweat lodge of the years.

ॐ

Jack of Hearts

Andrea Lewis

Thomas locks his bicycle on the back porch at midnight. The lights are still on in the kitchen. That means Joanna waited up. That means good news.

She is by the sink watching him take off his shoes. When their eyes meet, she nods. She is smiling.

"How far along?" he asks.

"Only six weeks. But I was sure. Everything smells funny." Joanna picks up a hard yellow sponge from the sink. "This smells like rotten fish. I could barf," she says, laughing.

Thomas takes her in his arms. Maybe once before in his life he has felt this happy—when he segregated his first marker gene, for the mutation called *jack-of-hearts*.

"Have you told your mother?"

"No," she says. "But now I have to call her."

"At midnight?"

"I have to. I'm too excited." She kisses him and goes to make the call.

Thomas takes an apple from the blue bowl on the table and cuts it in half. Joanna's voice from the living room comes in short, happy bursts as she tells her mother about the baby. She says she'll keep teaching at the kindergarten until her due date next April. Thomas stares at the cut-open apple, at the sad face of the seeds in their endocarp. The simplicity of it is beautiful. But as he looks at it, a strange panic overtakes him, starting in his solar plexus and radiating out to fill his gut, his arms, his legs. In his lab at the university, he tracks the growth of zebrafish, mapping genes to mutations. It is his job to make things go wrong with embryos. As he puts the apple on the drain board, he notices his hands are shaking.

He wants Joanna to get off the phone. He ambles into the living room, hoping an easygoing gait will kill the fear. He kisses Joanna on the back of her neck. Her conversations with her mother always bother him anyway. She lives a few miles from them in Philadelphia. The two of them communicate in cryptic phrases that sound to him like a feminine conspiracy about his own weaknesses, most notably his habit of working far too many hours.

"I have vitamins," Joanna is saying. Thomas kisses her neck again. He stretches her sweatshirt off her shoulder and kisses the hollow of her collarbone. She turns and slides her hand inside his jeans.

"Right, Mom, I promise." The innocence of her telephone voice, while she draws her hand over his growing erection, excites Thomas even more. Joanna hangs up. They peel clothing and make love on the living room rug.

Afterward, with beige carpet fibers poking the side of his face, Thomas thinks about implantation. He wants scientific fact to override his fear. He's dealt with zebrafish for so long, he has to think back to human embryology. A few weeks ago, the embryo, their embryo—well, to be accurate, their blastocyst— was an eight-cell soccer ball finding its way down a chemical path to the uterine wall. It burrowed in and began to divide. By now, thousands of generations of cells are hard at work. Messenger RNA is handing out assignments like a foreman in a factory: heart muscle, bone marrow, neurons. But the panic reappears when he thinks about the peril woven through the whole process. At any given moment, the baby's future might depend on one fragile electrical charge or chemical bond. Joanna stirs, rests her forehead in the middle of his chest, and says, "You're thinking about cell division, aren't you?"

In the lab, Thomas tells Roland the news. "Chief, that's great." Roland shakes his hand, then bear-hugs him, then shakes his hand again and won't let go. "That's fantastic." Roland is his top post-doctoral researcher. He beams his huge, white smile at Thomas. His eyes are shiny with joy. "A baby," he says. "A big, fat baby. I can't wait."

Roland's father is from Nicaragua and his mother is from Zimbabwe. Thomas has never met them, but would love to see the genotypes that resulted in Roland's tooth enamel, Roland's broad chest and six-foot build, and his endless capacity for work and enjoyment. He is always happy, always ready to tackle anything in the lab that will help their research.

"Everything in ten-C is ready to segregate," Roland says, referring to a new crop of zebrafish embryos. "Want me to get started?"

Roland's zeal for work reminds Thomas of his own grad-student days, before he met Joanna. He thought nothing of sixteen-hour stints in the lab. Sometimes he slept there. His social life narrowed to a few desperate dates with a brilliant coworker from Switzerland who earned her doctorate the same time he did. Claudine was smart, serious, and determined. They would work side-by-side to the brink of exhaustion. Once in a while, as if to prove they were still human, they'd go to a movie, sleep through most of it, and end up at either his tiny apartment or Claudine's bleak cell in student housing. His most vivid memory of those times was how white her skin was. Her body was much too thin from overwork, almost an adolescent's body, although womanhood asserted itself in her large brown nipples and sensuous white neck. She had a womanly appetite for sex too, but was content in its aftermath to lie in bed discussing embryonic cardiogenesis or T-box gene expression. Claudine returned to Switzerland with her Ph.D. and married an x-ray crystallographer. Thomas still reads her papers and follows her research. A year ago, when he isolated *jack-of-hearts*, she called to tell him she was citing his results in her work.

Thomas wanders into the lab where Roland is updating the tag on one of the plastic fish tanks. Fifty striped, silvery zebrafish, each about an inch long, dart back and forth in the water. Roland slides the tank back in the rack and mops every spilled drop with a clean cloth. Thomas admires his thoroughness but sometimes wishes he would move faster. They rarely talk about it, but time-pressure permeates everything they do. Pressure to design studies, produce results, get things published, and, ultimately, get funded.

"Have you tried the new scope?" Thomas asks. They have spent the last of their current grant money on a new dissecting microscope.

"Yeah, it's great." Roland beams his smile again. "I set it up for you this morning."

As the weeks go on, Thomas finds it more and more disturbing to look through the dissecting microscope at a transparent zebrafish embryo, its tiny coiled fist of a body, its long accusing point of a tail. The panic returns whenever he probes the barely-developed aortic arches, looking for the effects of an induced mutation. In *jack-of-hearts*—so named because the mutation hijacks the heartbeat—the embryos die quickly of arrhythmia. In *miles apart*—named by a researcher who missed his distant girlfriend—the two heart buds never join across the midline to form a whole heart. In *hands off,* the transcription factor Hand2 switches off and the ventricles never have a chance. In the city of the cells, he sees continual destruction. The chemical wrecking crew can bring down any structure. A tiny bomb of one molecule can blow up a bridge. The earthquake of an altered gene can flatten everything in sight.

The Saturday after Thanksgiving, Thomas drives Joanna and her mother to an Amish village in the country. Joanna is beginning her fifth month. She wants to visit a little shop that sells hand-made cradles. Thomas has been in the lab every day, including Thanksgiving, for the past six weeks. He yawns while a thin carpenter with a ragged beard discusses oak and pine, grain and sanding, staining and finishing. Navajo flute music drifts from a CD player. Blue and yellow mobiles of fabric lambs and helicopters, made by the carpenter's wife, hang everywhere. At every new item, Joanna's mother, Virginia, exclaims, "Isn't this darling?"

Thomas bumps his head on a mobile, disrupting his thoughts, which are on S1P molecules and their receptors, the chemicals that bring the embryonic heart buds together, like the two sides of a child's valentine, to form a complete heart.

"Thomas, which one do you think?" Joanna asks. Apparently Joanna and her mother have narrowed the choice to two cradles.

"They're both great," he says. His enthusiasm is so hollow that Joanna turns from him and takes her mother's arm. Thomas detests their collusion. Virginia has supported Joanna in her decision to refuse amniocentesis, refuse to learn the gender, refuse to know anything outside the realm of their female certainty that all will be well. When the panic comes upon him, Thomas wishes he could draw a picture for them of a spine that has stopped growing or a lung that never opens. He wants to explain to them the effect of one mutant allele, one unexpressed enzyme, one rogue cofactor. He wants to tell them about *throbless*, in which the heart looks perfect, but the proteins that make it beat are missing.

By evening, Joanna is still angry. When Thomas lies next to her in bed, she turns away from him just as she did in the store.

"I'm sorry about the cradle," he says.

"It's not the cradle. You know that."

"Okay, then what am I sorry about?" He tries to put his hand on her shoulder. She jerks the blanket up to her ear, pushing him off.

"For starters, you're never here," she says.

"I'm just trying to finish some things. I could get a whole set of results wrapped up before the baby. If I keep going."

"Do you even want the baby?"

He stares into the dark and waits for the panic. It usually burns for a while, like an ember in his chest, and then radiates out, sometimes slowly, sometimes all at once.

"I want the baby." He tries next to sneak his hand onto her belly, but she is ready for this advance and shoves him away. He has never told Joanna about the fear. He doesn't want to, but he finds himself saying, "You know, I see this stuff in the studies, these…mistakes. I mean there's so much that can happen." To his surprise, he feels a little better, talking about it. He wants to put it just right, if he can find the words, so she'll understand.

As if sprung from a trap, Joanna jerks upright and twists around to look down at him in the dark. "This baby is not a lab fish," she says. "This is our child. You are the father."

The word father conjures for him an absurd memory of a textbook drawing of sperm, those whip-tailed BBs of desire. He was maybe nine years old the first time he saw such a drawing. Before he can prevent it, a little laugh escapes his lips.

"You think that's funny?"

"No, I don't." But he still feels like laughing. He feels a little hysterical. He reaches for her, but she lies down and gives another savage jerk on the blanket. "I want to be a father," he says weakly.

"Good." Again her back is toward him, her spine rigid with fury.

Thomas cannot sleep the rest of the night. Exhausted by the fear, he gets up at four in the morning and dresses in the bathroom. Just as he's unlocking his bicycle on the back porch, Joanna clicks on the kitchen light and comes to the door.

"What are you doing?" she asks.

"I couldn't sleep." He fiddles with the bike lock. "I thought I'd go in."

She looks at him. Her eyelids are heavy, and one side of her face is a little dented from sleep. "Have fun," she says, and goes back to bed.

He arrives at the lab at four-thirty to find Roland already there, tapping at his computer keyboard and peering into the screen. He is so engrossed he doesn't notice that Thomas has arrived at work three hours earlier than usual. By way of greeting, he pulls a sheet from a messy stack of papers at his elbow and says, "Chief, look at this."

A fax came in during the night. There is an opening at this year's Developmental Biology Conference in Zurich. They are invited to present the results of their study. If they can be ready in four months.

"But look at the dates," Roland says. "It's right when the baby is due."

Thomas studies the fax. He notices from the tiny print at the top that it came from Claudine's lab, although her name does not appear. He wishes Roland weren't standing there, because he wants to count weeks on his fingers. But there is no getting around the opening date of the conference. April 14. One week before the baby is due. Maybe the baby will arrive late, he thinks.

"I should go to this," he says.

"Are you sure?" Roland asks.

"Look at the people who'll be there." Thomas points to a list of ten or twelve headliner names. "We can't pass this up." The unspoken part is that any one of those names could end up with the grants they need to keep going.

"So, I should say yes?" Roland asks.

"No, I will."

He emails Claudine. But he can't wait for a response, so he calls her. Yes, she sent the fax. "I thought you'd be interested." Her French accent reminds him of all the long hours in the grad-school lab. "Someone dropped out," she says, "so I told them to offer you the opportunity." Claudine talks about the work she is doing. As always, her studies sound like beautiful, spare pieces of art, elegantly designed and meticulously carried out. Suddenly, by comparison, his own study feels cumbersome and burdened with the wrong details. He pictures Claudine in her pristine Swiss lab, surrounded by gleaming instruments that are somehow more advanced than his. Before he is even off the phone, he feels new pressure to finish the study before the baby is born. Tabulate the results before the baby is born. Go to Zurich. Make it back before the baby is born. No matter how hard he tries to shove the panic aside, it creeps back and lurks about, a thief checking for an unlocked door.

To get it over with, he tells Joanna that evening, straight out, that he has a trip to Zurich on April 14. She says nothing. She walks to the phone and calls her mother. In a loud voice, she asks her to come and stay with them.

Virginia moves in the week before Christmas and quickly takes charge. She bustles from room to room. She makes beds, stacks magazines, scrubs vegetables. She accompanies Joanna to the doctor, to the mall, to the movies. As soon as Thomas is free of these responsibilities, he wants them back. His guilt doubles. He wants to show them he can change. In a burst of resolve that lasts one week, he breaks away from the lab earlier, comes home earlier, and makes vague efforts to help out. These only amuse and annoy Virginia. She smiles and shakes her head while taking a paring knife from his hands or refolding a t-shirt. Still, he feels compelled to prove his worth to his mother-in-law. He shadows her into the laundry room, the kitchen, the garage, hoping to be of use, as though he were an ailing, half-deaf collie who fears his master may soon put him down.

"Don't make up with me," Virginia tells him. "Make up with your wife."

He tries to explain to Joanna about the conference—who will be there, the competition, the pressure. If he doesn't get grants, he can't continue his research. She knows this. But ever since her mother arrived, Joanna has changed. She has a new distance from Thomas. She treats him with bored patience, as she would a house guest at the end of a too-long stay. While he delivers his rambling explanation, Joanna rubs spray wax into the dining room table, pausing occasionally to scratch a stuck particle of food with her fingernail. Finally she looks up. Thomas fears for a moment she might point the spray can at his face.

"Can't Roland go?" she asks. "He knows as much about it as you do."

"Roland's great, but—"

"I know. He can't speak at meetings."

It is Roland's one weak point. He has paralyzing stage fright, Thomas knows. The last time Roland tried to present a paper he almost fainted.

"You know," Thomas says, hearing his own pathetic rationale, "this is for the baby. If this works out and we get some funding, I can relax."

Joanna takes one more swipe at the table and walks away.

In Zurich, everything is orderly. The trains run on time, the streets are swept, the storefronts gleam. The hotel towels are plump and downy white, and the hotel soap sits in the center of its ridged, ceramic dish. Thomas feels like a bear in a dollhouse—too large and too clumsy for this tidy, compact country.

The conference's first-night wine party is underway in the hotel ballroom. The vast space thrums with the voices of three hundred scientists arguing at once.

Thomas sees Claudine. She stands next to a long table that holds a single cheese tray, stripped now to its parsley sprigs and grape stems. Three young men who could be triplets in their grad-student chinos and crew-neck sweaters form a semicircle around her. She is talking very rapidly, in French. The young men lean in to hear her every word. They are as gawky and eager as baby owls. One has a clipboard propped against his skinny hip and takes notes. When Claudine emphasizes a point with her plastic wineglass, all the baby-owl eyes follow it, transfixed.

She sees him and breaks away from the group. "Thomas, how lovely." She kisses him on both cheeks. He breathes in her scent, which is like Switzerland itself, scrubbed clean with lavender soap. In their brief embrace, Thomas feels the tiny bones of her shoulders under her trim black suit. "It's so good to see you," she says. "Isn't this awful?" She looks over the noisy crowd. "I think people are having perhaps too much wine."

They find the hotel restaurant, cavernous and candle-lit, empty before the dinner hour. Claudine orders for them in German. The table is laid with a thick, white cloth, heavy silver, and a small crystal forest of wineglasses.

"Philippe didn't come with you?" Thomas asks.

"No, of course not." Claudine sounds angry. But her mouth quickly softens back into a smile. "Philippe detests these things."

"Who doesn't?" Thomas laughs.

She looks at him, puzzled. "You mean you did not wish to come?"

"It's not that," Thomas says. "But you two are the power couple of Swiss molecular biology. Everyone expects to see you together."

The waiter arrives and shows Claudine the bottle of wine she ordered. She points impatiently at their glasses and he pours. In the silence that follows, Claudine lowers her eyes and aligns her silverware. "Philippe and I are no longer together," she whispers. "He is leaving me."

"You're kidding," Thomas blurts.

"I'm afraid not."

"I'm sorry. I didn't know."

"Well." Claudine lifts her narrow shoulders and drops them. "It was coming for some time. He wants children and I do not. What can I say?" She looks at him, her dark blue eyes questioning whether he will judge her harshly. "I cannot stop my work now. Not for a baby."

"No."

"Sometimes I think scientists should never have children."

The waiter brings their bowls of onion soup. Thomas hunches over his and stabs its bread-and-cheese crust with his soupspoon. Dark blotches of broth leak out and spread on the cushiony white tablecloth. "I guess I haven't told you," he says. "I'm having a baby. I mean, we are. Joanna is."

"Oh, Thomas." Claudine brings her hand to her white throat. Once again, she aligns her perfectly aligned silverware. "Of course, for you, this is… for you, I extend congratulations." She leans forward and grabs his wrist. "Really."

"It's all right." He feels her small fingers on his pulse. Her forehead is very white where the roots of her dark hair grip the skin.

"For you, it is different," she says. "You are the man. The husband."

"No, I've been worried about this," he says, to his great relief. "I've been working nonstop. I haven't even—" He breaks off, suddenly hearing that his own voice is near tears.

"No, I understand," Claudine says. "When we started the mutagenesis screen, I never wanted to leave the lab. I had a cot there."

"You did?"

"Of course. Philippe thought I was crazy."

"That's what Joanna thinks."

"But look what it accomplished. Labs all over the world use results from that screen. The work was critical."

After dinner, Thomas intends to walk Claudine back to her room. Yet before long, he finds himself in her room, kissing her white forehead and her pale eyelids. He loves even the fine fabric of her jacket as he runs his hands over her back. She clings to him with a force astonishing in one so small. They have their old script for this, and Thomas wants it to be that uncomplicated. But later, in bed, he hears Claudine crying in the dark. He puts his arm around her. She doesn't move. "You should go," she says into her pillow.

At ten o'clock the next morning, Thomas enters the lecture hall just as Claudine begins her talk. He finds a chair in the back row. He is afraid if he sits too close, the others might detect a force-field of guilt from the night before. When he arrived in Zurich, he had been jealous of Claudine's work and anxious to hear her presentation. Now he feels like a schoolboy who might miss the lecture because he has a crush on the teacher. He catches himself watching the buttons on her blouse instead of the slides on the screen.

He isn't really listening, but he hears Claudine mention *jack-of-hearts*. She and her team have worked with over fifty heart mutations, some commonplace now, such as *jack-of-hearts*, *miles apart*, and *throbless*, and some new ones, such as *toughluck*, *croaker*, and *seashell*. They have isolated proteins, lipids, and enzymes that control every part of the heart. "We have even surgically removed part of the fish-heart ventricle," she says, going to a micrograph that shows, in a map of blue and red dyed cells on a black background, the microscopic incision. "The surprise was, the heart restored itself. The cells had a mind of their own. They knew what to do." She smiles out over the audience. "The cells said, 'We need more heart muscle, so let's build it.'"

Thomas has heard of this phenomenon. His lab has never attempted to recreate it. They don't have the equipment. But Claudine's next slide—the heart undergoing its own repairs, the new green cardiomyocytes seemingly eager to fill in for the missing cells—rivets his attention. These are beautiful cells, each one holding the unknown, as all cells do. That is the mystery at the center of his work: cells with a mind of their own. Cells removed from an organ will try to team up and behave like the organ. Cells left alone in a dish will replicate and try to organize a safe and useful pattern. Even the brand new, fledgling cells of a blastocyst, he remembers now, will not hesitate to find their home in the wall of the uterus, where all that oxygen awaits them. He remembers lying on the carpet thinking about the blastocyst nine months ago. And now the baby, with its heart and lungs and neurons no doubt intact, is ready for its journey. Has a mind of its own.

Claudine's study is certain to be the most elegant of the conference. She finishes by announcing that a drug company in Geneva is already finding medical uses for one of the proteins she has isolated in the embryonic heart. She receives a huge ovation. Thomas wants to congratulate her, but does not want to join the lemmings that rush to the stage to talk to her. He is near the door, so it is easy to slip out. It is even easy to return to his room and stuff everything into his small suitcase and run out to the street like a criminal making an escape. He takes a cab to the airport and gets his ticket changed. Although it seems the young man in the red airline jacket will never stop typing the keystrokes that will get Thomas home, he is at last striding to the gate.

Before he boards, he calls the house. Virginia answers. She tries to keep a clinical tone, but cannot truly contain her excitement because she is about to take Joanna to the hospital. The urgency in her voice creates in Thomas a physical craving to be there with them.

"Her water broke twenty-two minutes ago," Virginia says brusquely. "We're just getting her things together."

On the plane he calls Roland. "Can you pick me up at the airport?" He is in a middle seat, shouting into the phone while his neighbors stare. "I need to get to the hospital."

On the other end, Roland lets out a whoop of delight. Then he seems to remember what day it is. "Wait a minute. How did the paper go?"

"I didn't give it."

"You didn't give it?"

"I found out about Joanna. I had to leave." Not exactly true, but he tells himself he'll explain it all to Roland later.

Roland is waiting in his car, engine running, smile so huge Thomas sees only his teeth through the windshield. It is close to midnight. Thomas wonders which date will be the baby's birthday. He leans forward as if it will make the car go faster. Roland is driving very cautiously through the empty streets. "We'll get there," he says, though he stays at the speed limit. But close to the hospital, at a deserted intersection where the light takes too long, Roland slips through on red.

"Don't take any chances," Thomas says, laughing.

Roland drops him off at the hospital's main entrance. Thomas takes a slow elevator to the fourth floor. As he pushes against the metal bar on the glass door marked Obstetrics, he sees Virginia walking down the hallway. When their eyes meet, she nods. She is smiling. Thomas runs to join her. He feels the fist of his heart uncoil and open toward his wife and child. &

How Suffering Goes

Melisa Cahnmann

I sit. The ache in my calves and ankles is severe.
I watch the monkey scratch my mother's head. Mother says
she has a headache. The monkey is laughing.
She says she has a sharp pain in her eardrum where the monkey
has pinned his long pink finger and stuck out his tongue.

From the far right corner of the room someone sneezes. I hear it.
A car engine, a cough. There are needles in my toes.
The Insight Meditation leader says to name your feelings.
I had car rides with my mother in mind. Naming
and holding herself one part at a time. She punctuated silence
with *stomach, stomach, stomach* and *neck, neck, neck.*

An abbreviated story of two failed marriages and a childhood
of bandages. Self pity like a cool, wet rag pressed to her forehead.
The meditation leader says it's best to catch the pain early,
when the unpleasant sensation arises, to come back to breath.

I am in the car with her and the unpleasant sensation arises.
I remember her beached body under afternoon blankets and bottles
of prescriptions willing to concede she was *sick, sick, sick.* The leader
says to name feelings three times before we scratch an itch, lift
a numb leg, or brush a stray hair from our face.

I sit in the car and say: *pain* again and again. Still it's there
where my face is *aversion* and *suffering* in the side-view mirror.
We climb stairs to our destination, and she cries
three times about her knees. Her chant is a haunt that echoes
from closets of old clothes, old minds

like old monkeys, always moving, scratching, knocking on glass.
I hear them. Their laughter, a group of girls running through
the apartment hallway. Rain falling over the porch. A change in light.
A small tremble of breath across the upper lip,
again and again and again.

∞

After Reading a Letter from My Mother

Melisa Cahnmann

There she is again in the mail, her loopy o's and dotted i's
and her itsy bitsy teenie weenie song from the front seat
of the green station wagon, her bottles of lotions, her heating pad
and moans: she comes out of the envelope like plastic tumblers
stuffed into a closed cupboard, she comes like dusty cans
of cream of mushroom soup. There she is again, she who means well,
who sings in the car, who buys too many cans. She whose bathroom
was a palace of make-up and cream, she with her ice cubes
and coatless winters. The heat of her *one eyed one nosed flying
purple people eater.* She is reading Tom Clancy. She is screaming
at doctors, she who tucks me in and says I can stay home
because I'm sick, we're all sick and we are a house of witches
who dance in the living room in our underwear to Carole King
who makes the earth move. She is here again, she who was my first god,
she who is resting under an eye pillow, she who is not to be disturbed:
she and I will be sleeping in late tomorrow.

∞

The Levitron

Robert Oldshue

Let me tell you one thing: these know-it-alls who come around hawking computerized this and that to make Shady Rest work like the Holiday Inn have never worked in a nursing home. They've probably never even been in one and figure they never will be, which is why they're so sure they can help us. In the million years I've been a nurse here, Mr. Hofstedder, our director, has fallen for gizmos that do everything from medicating to exercising our patients. He even got one to *visit* our patients: a box that made life-size holographic images of any visitor a patient wanted, however frequently and for however long. A busy loved one would pose for an image and record a set of nurturing phrases that could be updated by telephone as needed. A nurse who'd completed the required in-service would program the box and place a control within the patient's reach. And like most of these gizmos, it was a perfectly reasonable idea. But Mrs. Wembly dialed up a vision of the welcoming Christ that strolled to the nurses' station, causing a general tumult on 2-West, and Mr. Johnston managed to dial up a Playboy Bunny.

Then there was the flying vital-signs machine. To save us the trouble of going from patient to patient taking blood-pressures and temperatures, this little wonder zipped around Shady Rest, identifying patients by sonographically determined skull shape until it tried to take a temp on the guy fixing our elevator and he beat it to the floor with a crescent wrench.

But the worst was the Levitron, what Mr. Hofstedder called "an end to all our troubles." He was beaming the day he called us to the training room and introduced a Ms. Somebody who had a little too much hair, a little too much smile, and clicky little heels that made her satin bosom jiggle when she walked. As if me and the other girls would be impressed. As if we needed to be told that falls were a big problem for our 'clients'.

"And then there's *you*," she said as if she spent all her free time just worrying about us. She pointed to a machine we would have been looking at and wondering about if we hadn't seen so many machines of so many shapes and sizes. This one looked something like a Zamboni, the thing they clean ice rinks with, only smaller, more the size of a sit-on lawn mower, and she said you could ride it and drive it around but that was just for applications in the field.

"The military designed it to move casualties out of battle. They had no idea it would revolutionize patient care," she explained. *"Think of it,"* she kept saying, as if none of us thought until instructed to do so. "You've got a patient with vomiting or incontinence, or the patient's demented and spills all their food. The patient's a mess and so are you if you have to wrestle him to the shower and into a new set of clothes. But what if you could make the patient float? What if you could push a button and the patient would rise from the bed and stay there until you changed the bed and changed the patient? What if you could float the patient down the hall to the shower, then float them back to bed?" She switched on the machine, pushed a few buttons, and to our collective astonishment, Mr. Hofstedder began to float, an inch, and then a foot, and then several feet. She pushed another button, turned a dial, and he rotated slowly from an upright position to lying on his back, and then his front, and then his back again, and then she steered him around the room, around the cabinets and the light fixtures, before returning him, upright, to his chair.

"How was that?" Ms. Somebody asked.

"Wonderful!" he replied. "Very educational!"

"You can set the Levitron for any height you want," she continued. "The patient will feel nothing until he or she falls, which they won't because they can't. They'll simply float until you find them and gently push them back again."

She said the Levitron would be placed at the front desk and anytime one of us wanted to float a patient or to activate the round-the-clock Fall Guard feature, we'd simply come to the desk, input the patient's name, date of birth, social security number, and, of course, billing information, and everything would be perfect, which for several months it was. Our fall rate went to zero, as did our rate of fall-related hip fractures, scalp lacerations and less important injuries, so we were pleased, and Mr. Hofstedder was pleased, as were those family members who were initially somewhat dubious.

And some benefits were unexpected, like for Mrs. Bergstrom. She was so stiff, her family couldn't walk her or move her or do anything but sit beside her bed and look at her, but with the Levitron they could float her down the hall to the dining room and enjoy a Sunday meal. Yeah, it looked peculiar: there were her son and daughter-in-law sitting at a table, acting like nothing was wrong, and there was Mrs. Bergstrom, her head at the table and the rest of her sticking out half-way across the next table, but it was the first time she'd eaten in the dining room in over a year. It meant a lot to her, and it meant a lot to her son; it meant a lot to all of us.

And dear Mr. Claymore. When was the last time we'd heard him laugh or seen him smile? When was the last time his teenage grandsons had looked anything but surly when their parents dragged them in for a visit? But once we explained the Levitron, the boys floated him to the solarium and used him for a game of catch. As horrified as we were, you should have seen Mr. Claymore.

He called himself the first talking football. "Claymore has Claymore in the end zone and throws Claymore!" he said, grinning as he spiraled from one grandson to the other.

And the Levitron worked outside the nursing home almost as well as it worked inside. Families could take their previously immobile parents and grandparents out to the front garden or for a walk around the block. The anti-gravitational effect lasted for several miles. With the patients appropriately tethered—and the appropriate permissions signed and witnessed—families could stroll along the waterfront or through our city's parks, acknowledging the surprise of passersby with a healthy and often long-lost sense of humor. "This is mom," they'd say looking up the rope to a hovering elder as if they'd won her at a carnival. "She just flew in from Ohio." Or, "This is Uncle Ethan. He does this when he drinks a lot of soda."

And *we* felt lighter too, which in this line of work is the most anyone can ask. So often we trudge from one mess to another, from one multi-faceted and slow-moving disaster to the next and the next. Sometimes our legs feel like lead, our bodies feel like they're six times bigger than they're supposed to be, and all we can do is stand there and gape, and sometimes even that's a lot to ask. Try showering an eighty-pound woman who kicks and scratches you. Try doing it without breaking her osteoporotic bones. Try doing it without tearing or abrading or even bruising her paper-thin skin. Try changing a bed that's full of stool again an hour later, and the next hour, and the next, because the patient's not adjusting to the tube feeds that his doctor keeps insisting that he will.

For the first time, our jobs seemed doable, the patients and their families seemed agreeable and appreciative, and Mr. Hofstedder started calling us by name, which was nice even though he usually got them wrong.

"How about that Levitron, girls?" he'd say. "I think we're really on to something here."

But just as he was starting to discuss a raise, just as we were starting to feel that we weren't nurses because we'd made a mistake, or suffered some small but irrevocable accident of fate, there was trouble with the Levitron. First a little, then a lot, and then all of us were remembering just how horrible fate can be.

It started with Mr. Overstreet. He couldn't sleep, and the aides said he was tossing all night, but he insisted he was bouncing, bobbing like a cork in water, and several other patients said they felt the same, and while some of them liked it, most of them didn't. They asked if the Fall-Guard was set a few inches too high. We looked and didn't find anything, and didn't wonder until the first head injury. After months without an incident at Shady Rest, we were floating Mrs. MontLuis to the shower when she hit her head on the ceiling so badly she needed half a dozen stitches, and the family was upset. They complained about the Levitron, and we explained that as far as we knew, it was working as it had always worked.

But then Mr. Rosselli lost weight, and then Mr. Townsend and Mrs. Torres. All the patients were losing weight, and they weren't all malnourished, cancerous or hyperthyroid, or harboring another of the bodily wasting diseases. But the weights kept dropping and the patients kept floating in their sleep, and pretty soon they were all getting hurt on the way to the shower or the dining room or church or physical therapy. Still, we tried to fool ourselves. Still, we told the patients and their families that everything was fine: we'd looked at the Levitron, we'd looked at the instruction book, and the Levitron was fine. Everything was fine.

And then it happened.

I walked in one morning and found all the patients on the ceiling. There they were, bouncing along like so many birthday balloons. Many of the patients were frightened or upset, and we had to do something. We called Mr. Hofstedder and got the number for Ms. Jiggly Bosom, but the response was just what you'd expect: for Domestic Sales press one, for International Sales press two, for Service please hold for the first available incompetent. By the time we had him on the phone, he claimed to work for the company but hadn't heard of the Levitron, and the next guy thought it was a heat pump, and the next guy—a woman actually—said we were calling the wrong division, health care was at a different number, would we like to dial it ourselves or would we like her to connect us? Finally we reached a technician who'd heard of the Levitron and knew what it was and had a screen that told her what to tell us. We told her what was happening, and over and over she said the same thing.

"You've got the blue switch up?"

"Yes."

"You've got the yellow switch down?"

"Yes."

"And you've got the dial turned as far as it can go?"

"That's right."

"Then it really should be working. It shouldn't be doing what you're telling me."

You're wondering, of course, why we didn't simply turn the Levitron off, or pull the plug. Picture 78 old people falling from the ceiling to the floor. Picture them landing on linoleum, even if we padded it. So catch them, you say. Pull them down one by one and tie them to their beds until they're all down, and then turn the machine off. But this state, like every state, has laws against tying or restraining patients in any way, under any circumstances, including this one. Believe me, once word got out, Shady Rest was crawling with inspectors and officials of every type, but they wouldn't give us the slightest help and they wouldn't give us a variance, not without a hearing, and that would take thirty days, expedited from the usual ninety days. All they could allow was manual restraint which required enough people to pull each patient down and hold them, or lie on them, or sit on them, or whatever. But in most cases this required three or four people, and the Levitron was so severely hyperactive that several patients needed a half-a-dozen or more people. And you can't let just anyone touch a patient. It has to be a licensed professional or someone from the family or someone the family has specifically agreed to. We didn't have the staff and couldn't hire any on the spot even if we could have afforded it, and both the police and the fire department were called and looked around before saying they couldn't help us either. It would take the whole force. It would tie them up in one emergency and pose a threat to public safety.

We were left to call the families, which we did, and aside from the anger and worry we had to handle, it was hard to get them all in the same place at the same time, particularly since a lot of them were from elsewhere in the country. It was several days before we had it all organized, and by then there'd been the catastrophe we'd been hoping to avoid.

A delivery man brought a load of diapers and left a door open, and the day was hot, and the air-conditioning made a draft from the home to the street that carried out several residents. In a matter of minutes, they were the merest specks, high in the blue, summer sky, and we had to wait until they floated beyond the Levitron's influence and came to earth, hopefully slowly and safely, which, against all odds, is pretty much what happened. Mrs. Ventura floated to an adjoining suburb and landed in a garden party meant to commemorate the 35th wedding anniversary of a Mr. and Mrs. Gottlieb who were really very nice about the whole thing. Mr. Sullivan settled at the ball game which was fine except that some of the fans were less than responsible. I was too busy to be watching, but apparently he was batted from one part of the stadium to the next as will sometimes happen with a beach ball. And poor Mr. Alvarez stayed up until after dark and came down on an outdoor rock concert, and the audience thought he was part of the light show. Ironically, the one who fared the worst was the one who landed perfectly. Mr. Dworken floated to his son's house, and the next morning, when his son was making waffles for his wife and three children, he opened the window to cool the kitchen and in came his father.

"Hi, son."

"Hi, dad."

There was nothing else to say. They'd said it all already, and a lot of it they'd said at Shady Rest with everybody listening. It was the sort of thing we hear all the time. The son didn't want his father in a nursing home any more than his father wanted to be in one. But Mr. Dworken had been failing, his mind had been failing, and then his balance, and then he was walking around the neighborhood in his bathrobe. He was getting to be more than his wife could handle unless their son came over everyday and sometimes twice a day, but their son has the three kids, and his wife is involved with the older people in her own family, and I guess she's got something wrong with her stomach or maybe bowels or maybe she said it was uterine fibroids. Anyway, they'd put Mr. Dworken at Shady Rest but he'd been upset, and his family had felt guilty, and floating in the window that morning was like pulling the scab off a burn. When the son called, we apologized and said we'd be getting the place back to normal as quickly as possible and would readmit his father then. We explained that the spectacle of Mr. Sullivan being swatted around on national television had mobilized the rest of the required family members and authorized volunteers, and the next day was really quite a scene.

Relations who hadn't seen each other or spoken to each other for years were suddenly having to share ladders, climb on chairs and sometimes each other to reach the patients who, often enough, they also hadn't seen. Predictably there was a lot of complaining and several sprained backs and twisted ankles and knees but also some surprises, particularly when the time came for the head nurse on each floor to give the all-clear and Mr. Hofstedder finally turned the machine off.

It was like when a patient died. A family might have been complaining about the food, about the laundry, about the sweater or the slippers or the dentures they were sure we'd lost, which we should find or pay for. Sometimes a family would get so difficult, we'd start to feel resentful, even threatened. And then the patient would die, and we'd expect even worse, but it was almost always the opposite. No longer tortured, the family no longer snapped but instead brought us cards and flowers and chocolates and food they'd prepared. I'd seen this about-face in any number of families, but I'd never seen it or imagined it in all the families, all at the same time.

Once the Levitron was off, once the patients were back to being patients and the families were back to being families and we were back to being the nurses they were always complaining about but not yet—not for at least ten or twenty minutes—there was a wonderful and precious human moment. There were handshakes, hugs, thank-yous, fond stories, and apologies. There was some recognition, however brief, that whoever and wherever we are, we all live and we all die, although in between things can sometimes get discouraging.

But as soon as he was back in bed, Mr. Tomaczek turned on his television, and Mr. Halpner said it was too loud and turned his own television even louder, and Mr. Levin pinched Mrs. Hanratty, and Mrs. Hamamoto threw her lunch on the floor. The next day, Mr. Sherman punched one of the other nurses in the face and the family refused to believe it. She must have been provoking him, they said. What's the matter with you nurses? Don't they train you? Our father's not the kind who punches people for no reason so whoever he punched probably had it coming.

Within a few days, life at Shady Rest was back to what it always was, but after what had happened we weren't about to complain. We didn't complain when the inspectors came through with the variance we no longer needed. We didn't complain when a number of families took their loved ones to other facilities and then demanded emergency readmission when they learned about nursing homes being nursing homes and pretty much the same everywhere. We didn't even complain when Mr. Hofstedder said that he'd gotten through to Ms. Jiggly Bosom, and she didn't know about the Levitron, that she'd been reassigned to another product—Once-A-Year-Feeding—and she hoped we'd consider a presentation. "We'll hold it in the training room," said Mr. Hofstedder. "I think we're really on to something here. How about it, girls?"

And when you think of all the damage there could have been, when you think of all the patients who could have been injured either at the home or out floating around the city, there was really only one person who ended up any worse than he had been, Mr. Dworken. Last I heard he was still at his son's house causing problems. Several times, his son has tried to bring him back. He's loaded the old troublemaker into his car, strapped him in, and gotten as far as our parking lot, but he can't get his father to leave the car, can't carry him by himself, and under the circumstances, we don't feel comfortable helping him. Oh, we're willing to come out and tap on the windshield. We're willing to smile and say, "Hi, Mr. Dworken. It's wonderful to see you, sweetheart. Why don't you come in and play some bingo? Why don't you come in and let us make some hot chocolate?" One time, the son asked if we could use the Levitron to get his father from the car. We told him we no longer had it, we'd returned it, we were sorry but the two of them were on their own which was a hard thing to say and, I'm sure, a hard thing to hear. Not surprisingly, the son said what so many of our families say: you'd help us if you cared.

As if we don't care. As if we don't help. As if the Levitron would have helped. Believe me, we do what we can here at Shady Rest, but things are what they are, are what they always have been and always will be. As much as we might want to change them—as much as we nurses might wish *a lot* of things were different in the first place—bad enough like good enough, we've learned to leave alone. ဢ

Another Life

Susan Varon

I doubt whether picking my way
down the sidewalk with Betty Schack
(another cripple)
will lead either of us to glory,

we might as well sit on the side
drawing with sticks in the dirt,

Betty meticulous and careful,
I slashing and cutting the earth
with my expressionism,

our canes lying forgotten, rolling
their eyes at each other, imagining

they remember when they were new sticks
with the hope of being used for a gun or a doorjamb.

In my drawing I imagine being new, too,
demanding loudly of the world, kicking up clouds,
lustily calling for another life. Over our heads,

people are talking on cell phones
till the air is buzzing, we hardly dare
stand up into it, straighten our stiff joints,
look around for our canes and be startled
when they come dancing to us,
not knowing they've decided

they lucked out to be what they are,
to be allowed to stand upright and accompany us,
taking lessons in fortitude and grace,

in this city so difficult to walk in,
this city so worth it anyway.

&

So Much in the World is Waiting to be Found Out

Sariah Dorbin

A railroad of staples traverses my mother's head. When my eyes travel south I realize my mistake in seeking a better view; from her bed hang pouches filled with fluids the color of illness.

They have shaved the right side where the staples are, but the red hair on the other side has been left alone. My mother looks like Bozo the Clown only worse, Bozo with just half the wig and the bald part in the wrong place. Also the face is no good; I'd understood that the surgery was to relieve the swelling. By appearances, I gather they have simply taken the swelling from inside her skull and transferred it to the outside. They have also, I can see, replaced her makeup with a smear of purple across her cheekbone and temple. What the hell is wrong with these doctors?

Of my mother's talents, makeup ranked high on a rather short list, particularly that most difficult job—eyeliner. More than once she tried to show me the way, but to no avail. Ever since her first eye job, she herself had been blessed with that concavity above the eyelid typical of beautiful women: Sophia Loren, Audrey Hepburn, Catherine Deneuve. With this sort of eyelid, smudging was never a problem. But after arranging me and my frothy prom dress at her vanity and attempting to paint my eyelids for the first time, my mother had clucked with dismay over the way my lids rubbed up against themselves at the crease. "Just try not to blink," she said, and I wondered whether she might be serious.

Leaning against the cold metal rails of her bed, I look down at my mother's swollen eyelids, closed but somehow glaring at me. Even if I were able, I could not paint them for her now.

All I can do, it seems, is try to calm my breathing to match the ordered pace of her ventilator, and reach out my hand to stroke hers. It is limp from drugs or coma, I'm not sure which, and pale and crinkled next to mine, but our fingernails are identical: short, filed into careful ovals, and painted from the same bottle of milky-pink polish we share at our appointment each Saturday, which is always followed by a pair of decaf lattés—hers with Sweet & Low, mine with three sugars. This weekly manicure is one of the few pursuits my mother has shown interest in over the years. Since retiring from the Chanel counter at Neiman's, she has rarely left her condo except to trace a familiar route through Westwood on foot, seeking variety and friendship only in the formal, protracted chats she charms strangers into during their wait for dry cleaning or fresh baguette.

Life, it seems to me, never ponied up for my mother. But then, she stopped wanting things thirty-six years ago, when her agent stopped sending her out, her boyfriend stopped taking her out, and she went to the hospital instead, to begin my life as her own seemed to end.

Here we are, together in a hospital, again. It is the kind of place that makes it clear who is in your life. It is good for that. It is bad for that.

A man named David called me yesterday, while I was casting cats for a cat-food commercial. You'd be surprised how few cats are up to the job, which is simply to eat cat food with the lights on. David's job is to carry a very fancy cellular phone and to call people whose loved ones wind up in the UCLA emergency room. He must deal with noisy freakouts of all kinds in his ear, as well as abrupt silences, as he explains to multiple family members what happened to the loved ones and what the doctors have to say. I cannot believe how well he performed these duties when it was my turn—but then, he only had the one call to make.

Calmly, and with just the right amount of detail, David explained about the truck in the crosswalk, the various head and leg injuries and the not talking. After that, when I'd found my way to him after wandering through the labyrinthine halls of the hospital, he explained about the bleed in the speech center of my mother's brain. It was then that we made the joint discovery of my own legs not working anymore, at which point he gently took my arm and led me to a bank of plastic seats. His palm was remarkably dry.

Today, post-surgery, my mother has been moved to the Neuro ICU, a ward of twisted, twitching people who look as though they will be asleep for the rest of their lives. Most are young men, and though I cannot believe it of them in their current state, these are studly specimens, caught unlucky amidst acts of great daring. All around me lies compelling evidence against the wisdom of bungee jumping, motocross racing, extreme skiing. Also I cannot leave out walking to the hairdresser, the latest calamity sport.

At home, my three dogs follow me around until I remember to put on their leashes and walk them past the sad, chalky houses on my block. It is true that dogs save me in ways people cannot. Right now, for instance, I find myself hoping that all three dogs will shit on the lawn in front of number 2731 so that I can do something with my shaking hands.

Later, the dogs follow me into the bathroom. When they sit on the floor next to me, I place my hands under their wishbone-shaped jaws and feel the heaviness of their heads as they relax.

As I walk down the ramp that slices through the hangar-like space of the ad agency where I work, I see beneath me the tilted, furrowed face of Sean, my 24 year-old assistant.

"How is she?" he asks when I get to his desk. He holds the tension in his face while waiting for my answer. But I can't think of any words that would add up to an accurate description.

Much to my dismay, Sean has told me at regular intervals over the last year that he is in love with me, something I cannot accept as fact, given his youth and how far I feel from my own.

"Millsy," he says now, a riff on my last name. "Sweetie. Lunch?" He touches my forearm; I cringe at the moisture of his fingertips, which reminds me of the more awkward moments between us. No matter which reason I have offered him—the difference in our ages, our positions—he refuses to accept or believe it. "What's twelve years?" he said once. He thinks love is enough; that's how young he is.

I step back, and his arm falls from mine. I've discussed with him several times my need to not have it look as though we are sleeping together. Because we are not. "Messages?"

He hands me a stack of black-lined pink slips, which I flip through as I walk through the office. I feel about this place the way I feel about Manhattan or Chicago—nice places to visit, but I wouldn't want to live there. Sadly, I do live here, sixty hours a week at an orange desk inside a lime green cage, surrounded by other lime green cages housing orange desks. The agency produces crappy advertising everyone is embarrassed about. To make up for this, its founders have spent a large amount of money making the place look *happening* and *creative*, even when it is not. In this way, the agency itself is a kind of lie, much like the product it manufactures.

In fact, I do not actually *work* here. Other people, younger people in my group, do the work. I just look at the work and say *yes* or *no*. This is harder than it sounds, because even when I say *yes* a loud voice inside my head screams *No!* No, this will not win an award, the esteem of my colleagues, a ticket out of this schlock-factory. No, this will not lift me back onto the track from which I derailed somewhere along the line, who knows where. No, this cannot possibly be the sum total of my contribution to society.

Two guys are standing now in my lime-green doorway. The art director is holding oniony pieces of marker paper covered with little black boxes in which dumb things are happening involving a new kind of hair gel. He peers at me through his black stringy bangs.

"The Holdilocks thing?" his tall, beaky partner reminds me, in the questioning way that is supposed to sound hip. "We were supposed to show you yesterday?"

"We're going to play a game," I tell them. "For the next while—I don't know how long—we're going to pretend that I'm blind." I explain that they are to present their ideas to me over the phone, that I will be at the hospital most of the time instead of at the office.

On their way out, I hear the art director mutter to his partner. "Pretend?"

An hour later Sean follows me through the bright sunshine to my car. He stands still, holding my gear for the shoot in his arms, while I lift things away one by one: laptop, cables, casting tapes, production notebooks, and directories.

"I could quit," he says. "To help you."

"No," I say.

"You have a lot of important decisions to make. You'll need someone to talk to."

I don't like that he sounds grown up. Even in the parking lot, this place produces lies.

At the hospital, teams of people with advanced degrees have asked my permission for several procedures each day that I have been here. These encounters are a lot like those in the rest of my life—all I have to do is say *yes* or *no*, and though I always say *yes* here, it is not what I mean. *No*, says that other voice, the soundless one that is perhaps my real voice. No, this can't be happening. No, this is not my fault.

Only weeks before the accident, my mother had asked me to accompany her to the supermarket. There had been a scene involving a lack of artichokes and she'd been asked not to come back. Fortified by my presence, she'd apologized to the manager who, flicking uncomfortable glances my way, reinstated her privileges. This incident clearly pointed to some sort of slippage, a recent, insidious slide from her always-perfect manners. Now, sifting through my mother's bills—many of them apparently months overdue—I do not wish to consider my inattention, my lack of action on her behalf. You're on it *now*, I nearly convince myself. What can be done now?

Ortho wants to re-break the ankle before setting it. Plastics wants to insert a pump in the other leg to drain the wound. Neuro, concerned still with pressure in her brain, wants to operate again. Neuro also wants a g-tube, antibiotics, a trach for better suctioning. Neuro is very demanding.

In between the permission-seeking, I try to eat cafeteria soup that smells like the hallways, and attend to my ringing cell phone. Today the Account Person has played the commercial for the client without me, and the client is unhappy. "The first 28 seconds are fine," she tells me. In the last two seconds of the commercial, the cat was supposed to run into frame and pounce on a bowl of the client's kibble.

"What's the problem?" I ask. "He *pounced.*"

"Yes," she says. "But Jerry says the cat's not smiling."

The doctors' representatives approach me, wearing white coats and effortless composure, but the doctors themselves do not stop and talk; they do not have time.

When I finally demand to meet with a doctor, the conference room pulses with empty chairs and absences—relatives long dead or denounced; acquaintances un-nudged toward friendship; men retreated as from a bad smell (my father, the first of these, who perhaps led the way, held the light, posted the signs).

The woman from Neuro sits quietly but is somehow breathless, as if to say, "I'm here for you, but it's costing someone somewhere something." Her face is blank, feigning patience at my questions.

"We just don't know," she says for the fourth time. My mother may never speak again, or she may fully recover. The longer she stays in bed now, the longer she may be in a wheelchair later.

"Like forever?" I ask. "Is forever a possibility?" The doctor explains something about atrophy and muscle contraction that I can't quite follow. I watch her mouth move, try to square those pretty lips with the ugliness of her words.

"A likelihood?" I ask. "Or a possibility?" I try to imagine my mother with bad legs. Instead, I conjure a crisp March night a few years ago. My mother, striding well ahead of me along Wilshire Boulevard after a movie, kicked her still beautiful seventy-one-year-old legs nearly as high as a chorus girl's while singing *"On the Sunny Side of the Street."* She sang all the words without stopping her legs, even after the sky broke open and dumped sheets of rain.

The point of this meeting is a document I have read and until now have ignored. Drafted by my mother's attorney years ago, this document is a dinosaur of contingency, its wording vague and insubstantial where it should be intricate as lace.

Catastrophic is the word I am stuck on, the word I have come here today to define with the help of an expert. What, exactly, did my mother mean? Couldn't she—a woman who insisted upon butter knives and fish forks—have been more specific?

The doctor straightens her shoulders. "Most people," she informs me, "indicate specifically which treatments they do and do not want. Some draw the line at heroic measures."

"Heroic. You mean like emergency brain surgery?" My go-ahead on that seemed like a given at the time.

The doctor is speaking now in sympathetic tones about the burden of responsibility, even as she leads into yet another request, this time for something called a central line. They want to quit stabbing my mother with needles, to pump in her numerous medications through a single catheter. But this procedure has some risk.

It is like dealing with a crafty mechanic, when I know nothing about cars, but with the stakes significantly higher. I look around the room, my eyes resting on all those empty chairs. "Yes," I say. "Yes."

Each morning I rise out of bed with a sense of purpose that was never inspired by cat food or hair gel. Mired in insurance tasks and the beginnings of a lawsuit against the truck driver, I keep office hours in the hospital's 7th floor lounge. I sit in one chair, pile paperwork in another. I wonder how people ever got through things like this before cell phones.

The other people in the lounge seem happy to have the distraction of watching me lose my shit with the HMO my mother had apparently switched to only months ago. Today a grandmotherly African-American woman watches me as though I were a television show.

"You can't just go to any hospital you feel like," the insurance lady recites into my ear.

"I really don't think my mother *felt* like coming here." My voice sounds as though it has teeth. "But it was six blocks from where she was *hit by a truck.*"

"That was unfortunate," says the lady.

"Yeah, thanks…"

"Because UCLA is not in our network. So she needs to select a hospital that is."

"That's kind of hard to do when you're unconscious," I say, before I hang up.

My next call is from the lawyer I've retained, who requests proof that my mother's medical costs will exceed the driver's insurance coverage of $15,000. The bill for the first week is $73,875. This seems an extraordinary amount of money until I remember that the commercial with the unsmiling cat, which will never appear on the air, cost the Frisky Whiskers people $425,000.

Sean calls. He wants to know what I'm eating for dinner.

"She's not dead," I tell him. "You can stop being my mother."

We both take a breath.

"I'm sorry," I say.

"Are you getting any exercise?" he asks.

My mother, even after three weeks, continues to warrant a steady stream of nurses who care for her in 12-hour shifts. Each tends to her in a flurry of constant, small movements, as though my mother were a complicated gourmet dish. I like today's nurse better than the others; her taut body lends her actions a kind of precision lacking in the others. I sit in a chair against the wall and track her movements: suctioning my mother's lungs; replacing the bag of jade green paste that is her food; monitoring the numbers on the machines whose continuous, mysterious bleeps and clicks I cannot distinguish from the sounds of real emergency.

"Do you want to know what it means?" The nurse has seen me staring blankly at the screen of one of the machines and is offering to help. Each new nurse I've encountered has offered me a miracle, a story of recovery and resurrection that I find unbelievable. This one explains the numbers, shows me which one measures the pressure in the brain, which one reports how many breaths each minute my mother is able to gulp on her own, without the assistance of the ventilator.

"Seven," I say. "That's good, right?"

The nurse nods at the pink sponge lollipop she's breaking out of sealed plastic. I watch her as she holds the white stick and rubs the sponge part around inside my mother's mouth to clean it. Only after she's finished, will I lean over my mother for our daily, whispered, one-way conversation; if I don't time this right, as I haven't on previous visits, my stomach will lurch at the sight of green mucus worming its way along the corner of her mouth. And my stomach is already lurching at the sight of my mother's eyes, still clamped shut to what is left of her life.

When I leave for lunch, the too-tan head of Pink corners me at the elevators. He wants to increase my mother's antibiotics. The catastrophe of the accident is beside the point; all the places where they have stuck things into her are infected; there's still the pneumonia from too much lying down and now two different infections in her colon.

"So what you're telling me is that this hospital is killing my mother."

"We'll need your permission…" Pink says.

I laugh, but it comes out like metal scraping. "To kill her?"

He explains that the drugs *might* save her. Withhold them, he tells me, and I'll need to prepare myself.

This is my mother's life in the air between us, balanced there while I decide how to answer.

It is my life, too. Once again, I say *yes*.

I have been summoned to a conference room for an emergency meeting. The man at the head of the table clears his throat. "We have a serious problem," he says. "The Frisky Whiskers people have decided to contribute an idea: talking cats. They like this idea very much." This man is my boss, and so I have to listen to him.

"They would like it even more if the cats had British accents. They think one should sound like Michael Caine and the other, and here I quote Jerry himself, 'like one of those veddy propuh butluh types.'"

My boss rests his icy blue eyes on my face. "You have forty-eight hours. Go."

By the end of the fourth week, with still no sign of life from my mother, I spend my time at the window beside her bed, watching people steer their cars in circles around the top floor of the parking garage below. I listen to the cadenced vacuum collapse of the ventilator and eventually look down at my mother, at her hair, now—without her weekly Tuesday appointment—the color and texture of steel wool. Her mouth, which she cannot use to speak or eat or even to breathe, gapes in a kind of permanent disbelief.

My mother is fatally allergic to aspartame, which you can buy in bulk at supermarkets for diabetic baking. Later, when I go downstairs for coffee, I hesitate in front of the little packets that sit next to the plastic stirrers. Aside from the white sugar packets, there are two others, blue and pink. My mother's allergy has always led her to the pink ones, given her necessary allegiance to saccharine. I hesitate, and then slip five of the blue ones into my purse.

In my talking cat commercial, the Michael Caine cat—a ginger-colored tabby—chases his silver-tipped housemate away from their shared bowl of Frisky Whiskers with a switchblade. "Touch my grub," he says, "and I'll pop a cap in your arse."

After I present the storyboard to my boss, he asks if I'd like to take a leave of absence.

In the bed next to my mother's lies a young man whose beeping machines alarm me. On a window ledge bright with sunlight sits his father, who occupies this perch, no matter what time of day or night I visit the ward. I wonder why no one else visits. I wonder whether the son is allergic to anything, whether the father ever fondles the fatal substance the way I do the blue packets hidden in my pocket, as though they were sacred religious objects.

Hunched and shaking in my bed, the dogs' heads bent over me in contemplation and concern, I grieve my mother's death for weeks but it never comes. At the end of the seventh week, when the hospital is through curing, then causing, then curing again infections in her colon and urethra and lungs, after I have hissed at and fawned over its various doctors in involuntary fits of frustration and gratitude, my mother is pronounced recovered enough to be discharged. I ride along in the ambulance that will deliver her to the rehab facility. Her eyes, having opened, finally, just days before, bounce off me and roam around the white metal cavity carrying us through the speeding traffic. She looks at me and at the gleaming white interior with the same blank expression.

Walking down the bright hall of the rehab facility, I keep my eyes averted, for fear of seeing something I wish I hadn't. There is already plenty to not look at in Room 31, I keep my eyes down, focused on the sparkle of the linoleum. How can a place so full of illness look so clean?

My mother's roommate is an old woman whose mouth has collapsed from a lack of infrastructure. This does not stop her from screaming over and over three words that I cannot understand.

I would like for this woman's vocal chords to snap and for my mother's to stitch themselves back together. I would like to see before me a sort of speeded-up film version of events in reverse; I would like to see the metal tube slip out of my mother's neck, for the hole it leaves to become unmarked skin again; I would like her hair to grow and regain its color and for her mouth to move and have sound come out; I would like her to stop worrying at the fold of the sheet. I would like more than anything to leave this place right now.

In the interest of moving toward the door, I decide that my mother is in dire need of fresh flowers. Outside, after perusing whatever growth I can find along the borders of the patio, I pick one stem from each plant. Then, bracing myself, I return to my mother's room. I reach out to her once beautiful hands, now dry and gnarled, the nails chipped and yellowing. She looks up at me, her eyes blank, yet I somehow know she feels confused: *What are you, and who do you want?* After some effort I am able to pry open one of her hands and clamp it around a bouquet of rose, geranium, dandelion. By the time lunch arrives, the stems lie scattered in her lap.

After several weeks of work with the speech therapist, my mother regains some function with her hands. This does not seem quite right, but I'll take what I can get. When I watch one of the sessions, my mother gestures toward cards bearing pictures of everyday objects. She's asked to point to the thing that tells time, and her hand flicks backwards against the card with a picture of a watch. She raises her eyes upwards – *morons,* she seems to say. But when she's asked which one is something to eat, she chooses the hairbrush over the banana. I try not to make this mean anything except that perhaps my mother's eyesight is going. She's *seventy-three,* I remind myself.

The speech therapist is also working on my mother's eyelids. One blink means *no.* Two, *yes.* According to this system, my mother understands what happened to her, she knows where she is, and I am her ostrich.

After the session, I wheel my mother into the dining room. Three women sit at my mother's table. Lunch has not been brought in yet, and through the glass window I can see the attendants standing next to the cart, gabbing away. The youngest of the women—she can't be more than twenty—is swearing about this. The force of her words is at odds with her inert body, collapsed in the wheelchair like a question mark. A long strand of drool hangs from her mouth. *Motherfuckingbitches,* she says to her lap. *Fuckinggoddamnbullshit.* When I look down, away from her face, I see long, dark hairs covering her legs. This sight unfurls a heavy feeling I have kept folded up inside me for weeks.

One of the older women, wearing a dainty pink shirt, sits up straighter in her chair. She thrusts her shoulders back and opens her mouth. "Don't talk like that," she screeches. "I don't want to hear that kind of talk."

Neither do I. My eyes wander to my mother, who is staring at the comics lying on the table. What I want to hear is the kind of talk I was raised on; I want to hear about the significance of beauty, hear it made manifest in the peaks and dips of my mother's trilling voice.

They are on the fourth round of talking-cat presentations when I go back to work. I sit in the meeting while my team presents work I have not seen; the client is silent until the last presentation, which features the cats as hosts of a cooking show. They are making a *ragoût* with all the different meats in the cat food. The one the writer describes as the Anthony Hopkins cat is doing all the work, while the Michael Caine cat sits on the sidelines handing him ingredients and hassling him. In one of the little boxes, the writer points to him holding a rubber chicken between his paws.

"The chicken's a little chewy," he says.

The writer, in performing this line, sounds more like Groucho Marx than Michael Caine. After this, the only sound in the room is my boss's pencil eraser tapping against the conference table.

The client's face crumples as if he just smelled a fart. "A cat wouldn't say that," he finally yelps.

I stand up and lean over the conference table. "No," I say. "No it wouldn't." My hands twist up like claws. "Because a cat wouldn't say anything, except maybe, *I can't talk because I'm a CAT.*"

At the coffee shop near my headhunter's office I sit with a latté and the classified ads. I have Sean's voice in my ear, reaching like fingers through my cell phone. "I walked out on those bastards," he's saying. "I'm at the market near your house. Chicken or steak?" Sean wants to know. "Beer or wine?"

"Yes," I say. "Yes."

I realize I am qualified to do nothing except tell people my opinion about things I would rather not think about. Just for kicks, I try to find an ad for this. Along the way I realize that I've never understood what exactly a keypunch operator *does*. Sure, operates a keypunch. But what is that?

So much in the world is waiting to be found out.

After letting him grill me chicken and stroke my back before booting him out with an apology and a peck on the cheek, I lie in bed with thoughts about Sean. None seem the kind of thoughts that would make him happy. What does he want to do with his life, besides follow me around and hand me message slips or flowers? I imagine a future for the two of us, one in which he does the laundry and I take him shopping for new cargo pants. Such fantasies seem obscene, but not in the right way.

My mother grasps my hand when I offer it to her, strokes my fingernails. Later, while swallowing the pureed lumps of meat and peas I spoon into her mouth, she lifts her hand, fingers curled against her palm. She studies her nails, lets her hand fall to her lap.

At the bottom of my purse, next to the blue packets I have carried around these five months, is the bottle of nail polish I bring to the weekly manicure appointment we used to share. I pull it out, and in my hand it hovers in the air like a question.

My mother's eyes blink twice in succession. Maybe it's a speck of dust. Maybe it's *yes*. &

Living Will

Holly Posner

At doctor dinners the talk sometimes turns
to death. The dilemma tonight:
Better to stroke out fast in the A & P
or suffer a longer, gentler loosening of screws?
Like Iris Murdoch, the spine man says.
Brutal, his wife adds, (They've just seen the film.)
twenty-six novels, no warning signs…
In the end, we agree, it's less about losing the keys
than remembering what a key was for.

Ah, but if we're lucky, we'll see it coming, I say,
Look at Virginia Woolf—she made a choice.
The table counters with research stats,
new meds, and protocols, burying me politely
with indisputable data as once again
First do no harm circles its wagons.
But merlot's fueled my metaphysics.
It takes courage to drown yourself, I insist.
Shoot me before I'm thorazined to my chair,
name tag slung round my neck, all hollow-socket and drool.
The brain's a traitor, my husband counters,
it won't announce the if or when.

We ride home in silence,
wondering how we'll manage not to die
too soon, not to live too long.
Although he loves me I understand
he'll not be the one to whisper, *It's time,*
help me load my pockets down with stone.

∞

The Call

Sharon Pretti

My husband bolts to the hallway, presses
the phone to his sleep-flushed ear—*your father,*

a hemorrhage—hurry. I could say I leap
from the bed, scan the room for shoes,

keys, scribble directions, a room number,
my skin prickling with hope.

I could say I speak to him inside my head,
believing my words can lunge across

blacktopped highways, spring down corridors,
sail over side rails to the part of his brain

that hasn't gone blank. I could say my breath
doesn't snag on the sticks of my ribs,

my limbs aren't caught in the whirl
the bed makes as if it were a sea

dragging me under, my body doesn't
stumble towards the phone, fists

twisted in the folds of my robe. I could
say I listen to the voice rush

through the receiver, keep
from imagining a dark line of cars,

sprays of carnations, gladiolas, my palms
numb from rubbing the box where his ashes will go.

ॐ

Surgeon

Sharon Pretti

She guides the drill through
the skull of my father,
inserts the probe below
his glistening cortex,
steers it to the spot where
blood pools like fierce
rain in the grooves of a field.
She works at the crown
of his six-foot frame,
fingers urgent as insects.
Her eyes lock on the
heave of his chest,
the hue of his cheek
as fluid speeds from his brain.
He could have sprung from her
the way she watches a twitch
flutter his lip, listens for air
to surge through the tube
snaking his throat.
She seals him, scrapes bits
of blood that grip
his skin like bursts
of sea stars clinging to rock.
When she returns him,
she stays with us longer
than she has to, taps
her thumb on the
stethoscope's disk—lingers,
as if she wants to say
where she's been, the part
of him cleaved to her palms.

ಐ

Oh, Collage: A Story of Strange Vision(s)

Susan Bloom Malus

Why are there so many white cars, anyway?

We're in the country, in upstate New York. Irwin waits at the wheel while I run into a diner to get a cup of coffee. I'm backing into the front passenger seat, careful not to spill my coffee, when I hear a loud honking. I look up, right across the empty driver's seat, through the side window, to see Irwin waving at me from the next car.

We both start to laugh.

Because people in the country leave their doors unlocked, because my visual field is very small and my attention focused on the coffee, I'm sitting in the wrong white car.

This isn't the first time, and won't be the last, that I'll see only a bit of what I'm looking for.

We're in the country because we've just bought a country house. My visual field is small because, in 1995, I underwent surgery to remove a benign tumor, a meningioma, growing in my optic nerve. As a result, I suffer from a variety of visual distortions including unstable color vision. Still, I love looking at color. I'm seduced by it, sometimes enthralled. And the new house provides me with endless visual pleasure.

Perched on five wooded acres above a country road, it's a house of gracious, well-proportioned rooms, wood-floored and spare. Light flows in from all directions—there are picture windows, dormer windows, skylights, various doors to the outside—and highlights pale tints of rose, green, and beige throughout the house. As the day moves along, as the light changes, the colors gain and lose value, a process Irwin and I watch with fascination. Sometimes, in bright sunshine, all of the walls appear to be washed with white, at other times with the lightest hint of grey. Are these colors true? I don't know. It doesn't matter. Looking about is like taking a deep breath. But sometimes the light is so blinding that I wear dark glasses or a visor indoors.

On weekend mornings, we drive from town to town, to tag sales, church bazaars and moving sales, whatever is advertised, whatever we pass on our way. Over any single weekend, we look at so much stuff, in garages, driveways, yards, barns, churches and houses, that I'm dizzied.

We wander through Valatie, a nearby town with several antique and not-really-antique stores. I find an Indian scarf, crinkled, rectangular, semi-translucent, with intersecting rows of patterns and colors: squares, circles, thick and thin lines, lots of yellow with muted grays, browns, and blues, and small, irregular streaks of gold paint.

I also buy another scarf so sheer, so faintly yellow, as to be almost invisible.

And then there are the fabrics. I start slowly—a few old napkins here, a pair of gauzy curtains—and accumulate quickly. By the end of a month, I have a stash that includes a bolt of muslin so long we could wrap the house—Christo style—stained linen tablecloths, silk squares, pieces of lace, and decorative handkerchiefs, possibly organza, with delicate embroidery and rolled edges. I have no idea what I will do with all of this. I'm useless with handicrafts, a life-long deficit unrelated to my vision.

Since my surgery, my life is visually complicated. I have double vision and slow vision, but no peripheral vision.

I need extra time to identify, for example, the face of someone passing me on the street. A tiny blankness burns at the center of what is left of my visual field. In order to see a face, I have to look slightly to the right of it, which takes an extra moment of focusing. By the time I'm there, someone has passed, sometimes with a wave.

I take this philosophically. I'll wave back at anyone. And once I know a face well, it isn't a problem. It's getting to know it that's difficult.

The double vision is most confusing. When I move, everything I'm looking at moves too, the double images sliding farther apart as I approach them, one image slightly to the left and above the other. My brain has adapted and pays more attention to one image, but the other intrudes, particularly when I'm in motion, causing frequent confusion. I may, for instance, glimpse a street sign, lose it, then have to stand still and look around to locate it again. Perhaps that is why I so love to look at art books and catalogs. At anything that has shape and color and that stands still.

Without peripheral vision, I'm unaware of people cutting in front of me until I'm nearly on top of them, of unexpected objects like construction posts or even an outstretched arm. I walk into things all the time but don't usually get hurt, having trained myself to walk slowly. And because I'm polite, I apologize frequently, often not seeing to whom—or to what—I'm apologizing. Was it an object or a person? No matter. *Pardon me. Excuse me.*

Because of the double vision, I have little or no depth of field. In familiar situations, my brain does its best to reconstruct depth, so the world doesn't appear completely flat. These reconstructions, however, are not always accurate. I may step off a curb, thinking it deep, and find my foot smacking the ground because the step is, in fact, shallow. The angle of a slope can mystify me. I stumble over unseen objects or misinterpreted depths. I crack some ribs and break a leg. After that, I carry a walking stick so that I can test unfamiliar depths.

All of this is cumbersome to describe, perhaps more so than to live. It's also so uniquely mine that I can't imagine that I'm describing it fully. My vision is an anomaly, carved into my brain by the successive actions of a tumor and a surgeon. No one else has this particular configuration, this set of problems.

When I see the neuro-ophthalmologist, I describe the couch quandary. The couch we've bought is khaki green. Or so I think until a friend says, "What a nice color, that taupe," and another says, "I always like brown, it's so restful." I check the receipt; the color of the couch is called "putty." Irwin insists there is no such color as taupe, that it's a word used for colors one can't identify. Other than that, he is mute on the subject of its color, refusing to tell me how he sees it. I start quizzing everyone who comes in: what color is the couch?

"I don't know if it's taupe or green. Different people see it differently. I'm in the minority, but I'm not the only one who thinks it's a sort of khaki. The company describes it as putty."

The doctor stares at me, and I wonder if he's worried or if he himself doesn't know taupe from putty. Finally he says, "Let's wait until we get to the color field test." After I've taken it, he confirms that the color vision in one eye isn't normal. "How this manifests," he says, "varies with the individual."

As I collect fabric, I realize that I'm becoming interested in the idea of transparency, that I like draping one ethereal piece over another to see the visual effect. This is playful and relaxing.

The summer continues; my infatuation with color grows. Over the past few years, in reaction to the visual confusion that I inhabit, I've found it a great and pleasurable relief to stare at items that remain motionless. My love for museums, always strong, has grown accordingly, and I willingly receive every catalog the mail-order people choose to send me. Color can provide pleasure so powerful that it is almost a physical jolt.

When I try to explain this to friends, they look serious, almost mystical. Some of them ask strange questions, such as whether I've also developed a special sensitivity to unseen objects, as if I might glide around like a bat using radar.

Well, no. Although I wish I could. *Pardon me, excuse me.* It gets tiring after a while.

At the writing of this essay, it has been seven years since I've seen normally. I'm lucky, I've been told, because even though each eye has such a small field of vision, those fields are in the front. There are some people who have to walk with their heads turned sideways in order to see where they're going.

Still, lucky as I am, if you shine a light in my eyes, my pupils hardly contract. Doctors don't know why. Nor do they know why, when I'm exposed to light, my visual field becomes cluttered with the kinds of semi-translucent forms that you see when you close your eyes.

Once a fast reader, I now read with one eye, a slow process that provides many surprises. For instance, I read an intriguing sentence online—*This text is dangerous.* It reminds me of the sixties, of "Steal this Book." I stop to consider, then go back and find the sentence again, this time in its entirety: *This e-text is not copyrighted. The clearinghouse encourages users of this e-pub to duplicate and distribute as many copies as desired.*

How did I misread so completely? I'm not sure. My eye tends to eliminate middle words or phrases, an event I can't explain, and my brain takes license. Actually, I much prefer my version. Aren't all good texts dangerous?

On Sundays, I pick up the Independent, a local paper; Irwin takes the Times. When I look at advertisements or headlines, word-collapse occurs. Buy butter-built cabinets, I read. That one's easy. How about 30 Lincoln ear pennies? This takes some thought. Aren't pennies the sort of thing you're not supposed to put in your ear?

Of course, I know I've read it wrong, but I wait before looking back, trying to unscramble the acrostic. Giving up, I see that some company is selling sets of 30 Lincoln wheat ear pennies.

We're at a flea market where people sell jewelry, furniture, silverware, dishes, coins, rocks, leather goods, books. Much of it is junk. But then there's the fabric lady.

She's in her thirties, a friendly woman with a pleasant smile and a broad stomach. Her fabrics spill from tables, barrels, chairs, and bins: hundreds of old handkerchiefs, napkins, tablecloths, curtains, sheets, and more. I plow through and pile up an armful. I buy edged and unedged lace, three fussy antimaccassers that I would never drape over our furniture, more scarves in colors I don't wear, a great square of taffeta in muted stripes of greens, a fragment of gold lamé, and a hand-painted fabric border with black geometric designs on soft shades of russet. I still don't know what I'm doing.

In the years since surgery, my vision has reshaped me. I've developed new boundaries which in turn shape the way others view me. There are my visor and dark glasses and the walking stick. Sometimes, catching myself in the mirror, I wonder how this could be me.

In my prior life, I always insisted on doing at least part of the driving: as a feminist and as the daughter of a mother who never conquered a fear of driving, I viewed such participation as necessary. This was before surgery, of course, before we had any idea that anything was wrong. Once, when we were returning from Woodstock over a winding and foggy mountain road and I was unable to see clearly, I found myself leaning forward, gripping the wheel and muttering: why is anyone out in this weather? Why is everyone driving so fast when visibility was so terrible? Are we all crazy? Are we going to be killed?

Finally, after I had woven down the mountain, I pulled into the first parking lot, put the car in park and handed Irwin the keys. I was so terrified and exhausted that I had to close my eyes and sit in the rear for the remainder of the trip; I couldn't even look at the road.

I didn't know it then, but my identity had already begun to be reshaped. I was no longer a fast, confident driver. Like those elderly people whose vision deteriorates so slowly that they don't notice until they plow into something, it never occurred to me, or to Irwin, that I should have my eyes checked. As New Yorkers, we understood anxiety: once I figured out the cause of my hysteria, my driving would return to normal. Or so we believed.

Six months later, in January of 1995, I was diagnosed with the meningioma. These tumors grow very slowly along the meninges, or linings of the brain, harmless and undetected until they bump into something. Mine wasn't noticed until it became tangled in my optic nerve. By that time my vision had deteriorated appreciably although, like those elderly drivers, I hadn't noticed.

After the surgery, as I had been warned, my vision was confounded, although my acuity, with new eyeglasses, was restored almost to normal.

Months after surgery, on the subway with Irwin, I sat staring at a poster about safe sex. I knew it was about safe sex because there was a message to that effect running along the bottom. A small, red image in the center, however, confused me. When I thought I'd made it out, I leaned toward Irwin and asked him why there was a tomato in the middle of a poster about safe sex. He looked at the poster and then at me. He said, "That's not a tomato, it's a condom."

We were still in the early stages of our adjustment to this new life of mine and while I found the incident—and his punch line—very funny, he found it unnerving. He wasn't yet used to these visual mishaps and worried that, when I was alone, they would distract me and I'd fall off a subway platform or into an open manhole. But I never did.

Later in the summer, I visit with the neuro-ophthalmologist, this time to look at the results of my semi-annual Humphrey Visual Field Test. To take the test, I first sat on a padded stool with one eye patched, my chin on a plastic rest, staring into the bowl of a tabletop machine, the unpatched eye focused on a bright light in the center. I clicked a hand-held counter each time tiny lights blinked in the bowl. When I finished, the technician handed me a printout of my visual field.

"You see," my very kind doctor says, comparing this test to previous ones, "there are a few dots less here, but does it mean anything? I'm not sure." He smiles. "We'll check again in six months."

We're both worried. Annual MRI's have shown a line of something exceedingly small resting on the optic nerve, though nobody can say whether it's tumor regrowth or just some scar tissue. I'm afraid that if there's a next time for surgery, I'll wake to see nothing. And then how will I live my life?

"Well," he says, "if we get to that, we can consider pinpoint radiation. There may be some short-term memory loss or maybe some memory loss in twenty years, it depends…"

"Out of the question," I say, having spent a great deal of time with a dying friend, my best friend, after she had lost her short-term memory following radiation therapy.

"Did I have my tea?" she asked one day, looking at an empty cup.

'No," I said, "I'm just boiling the water now."

"Okay," she said. "I just thought, if I had it, that I'd want to know if I enjoyed it."

That set us off on the same laughter we'd shared since childhood. It's a memory I treasure. Still, I understand what a fragmented memory can mean. Fragmented vision is quite enough for one person.

Because meningiomas grow so slowly, it may take years to know what the tiny line of something is. And I know that no one is ever going to tell me that the suspense is over.

The fabrics I've bought now occupy a large basket. I like to spread them over the bed and shift them around, one over another; it's the translucence of one sheer fabric over another that attracts me. And then one day, at a tag sale, I pick up a worn hardcover book about making collages. My heart starts to pound. Feeling like a detective about to make a breakthrough, I open it with determination and excitement.

I scan through information about materials and some rules that I immediately feel free to break. The author warns that the artist should know the subject of the work before starting it. Don't muck around with materials, he says, and think you'll find your subject that way.

As soon as I read this, the book—with its rules and prissy tone—goes back into its sale basket.

We drive home with the trunk packed with our purchases. The window is open and the phrase, *oh, collage,* drifts with a breeze and settles into my brain. It rustles with the leaves, rolls along with the sound of tires on dirt and gravel roads.

It is amazing that I, a writer, have something I need to say without using words.

I turn my attention to collage backing. I buy a square of stiff, heavy white fabric used for embroidery. I squirrel away leftover screening from the porch, scraps of nonslip backing for rugs, swatches of a weblike industrial fabric.

At a hardware store, I gather folders of Benjamin Moore paint chips. The chips are a bounty of colors captured in neat shiny rows, each a sharply cut square, their names evocative: Jeweled Peach, Mexicana, Durango Dust, Caramel Charm. Each square can be peeled off easily, to be held up to a wall or window frame, to be set together to test color schemes. I run a finger over one row after another. Delicious to be able to look at so many solid, unmoving blocks of color.

I'm not ready to start the collage until one late September evening. Irwin has gone to bed early. The country air is cold now and all the windows are closed. I'm at the kitchen table, fabrics spread over it. Bach plays softly in the background.

With no idea of how to start, I look for an analogy in writing and decide to create a draft. I begin with white copy paper, scotch tape, a scissors. I select the Indian scarf because it's cheap, the paint chips because they're plentiful.

I begin by lifting off two paint squares, Orange Flame and Tile Tan, and taping them to a clean white sheet of copy paper. I then cut a raggedy piece of scarf small enough so that it fits across the paint chips and then some, leaving an uncovered margin of about two inches at each end. I lay it down, look at it, and understand what I'm doing. I secure the fabric with tape, cut two more pieces.

The second strip of fabric, placed below the first, covers three paint chips: John Deer Yellow, School Bus Yellow, and Equipment Yellow. The third covers four: Pizazz (a deep tangerine), Regal Red, Lemon Drop, and Brandy Flare.

I sit back and look. Not bad. But something is missing. My eye rests on a color called Mystic Gold. It's deep and solid and restful, the color of a dark, grainless mustard. I tape it off to one side, in the right margin, all alone.

I'm satisfied. I pack up the rest of the materials, sandwiching the "draft" between folders of paint chips. I turn the lights off behind me, go to bed, and fall into a deep sleep that lasts twelve hours.

My friend Gail looks at my draft collage and has a lot of questions. "Is this how you see?" "What is it like when you see the orange square?" "Is the scarf over the colors really like your vision? I thought you had glare."

Well, no, it isn't really glare. Or it is, but it's more like a glimmering visual clutter or shimmering screen. It obscures details, makes it difficult to see in bright or dim light, and causes the pages of books or newspapers to take on tints of green, blue, or yellow when I read for too long.

I tell her about how, when I see a color with great clarity, I'm struck, as in lovestruck, moonstruck, filled with elation.

That, I say, is the mustard square.

"The thing is," I continue, "the way I see isn't only a bad experience; it's also just an experience. And since no one else has this particular experience, because the results of meningiomas are so idiosyncratic, it's an experience that no one else can understand. Which I guess is why I needed to make this."

She says, "It's an experience that no one else can experience."

"Right. And this," I say, pointing to raggedy strips stretched over paint chips, my taped-down visual draft, "this is the best I can do to explain what it's like." She's the only person, aside from Irwin, who has seen it. The creation was cathartic; since then, I've had no desire to proceed to the final "draft." She stares at it for a long time. "Amazing," she says. Then we put it away and have dinner.

In writing this piece, I had to lift the fabric off the draft collage so that I could again see the names of the color chips. It was like peeking in or looking back, like experiencing a profound nostalgia for something that had just happened. It made me think that my vision really is a metaphor for at least a portion of my life and that this isn't so bad: that the draft collage has expressed and revealed some part of my life's idiosyncratic vision. What this vision is, I can't quite capture in words. It has to do with an appreciation of color and tone so deep that it approaches the state of being stricken (as if, ironically, by illness); it involves a strong sense of isolation that at its best is calm, creative, and independent. It is closer to the condensed power of poetry than to prose. It dwells in beauty and in process and in the present. If it has a name, I don't yet know it. ⟑

Weatherman

Shannon McNamara

The weatherman was right.
You wouldn't have known it yesterday,
out with the dog, looking west.
Yesterday's horizon was empty,
finger-shaped clouds touched only the lowest
folds in the northern mountains.
Yesterday Griffin's paws kicked an updraft of dust.
Black dog, brown hills, gray sage.
Remember the prediction?
Look west.
I don't believe him.

But this morning the landscape is utterly mutated,
White. White, with reaching trees and staid powerpoles
cut out in black. Black dog, perplexed at first by the snow,
plowing his nose into the stuff,
tasting it, then chasing after the sloughing off
of laden boughs and powerlines.
Falling in irregular clumps and then a branch sighs
with a fall-out avalanche.
Then he's running randomly, then in predictable
cycles, then off again, mindlessly excited.

I'm behind the window glass, laughing, laughing hard, outloud, alone.
At Griffin: in his snow-fomented madness, ears back with momentum,
legs flapping like a butterfly in full
effect. Like I haven't laughed in months.
The diagnosis isn't laughable.
Doctors *have* announced worse—but not to me.
Doctors and weathermen: those messengers of chaos.
Tomorrow's weather is relatively easy
to predict (so I should have believed him),
harder to predict further out.

Go out far enough and you're forecasting
seasons, not weather. Hell,
I could tell you it will get colder before it gets warmer.

"You'll get worse before you get better," one specialist said.
"There's no cure at this point," said another MD, "you learn to live
with it, make adjustments."
"It would be best if you didn't live alone at this time."
"Chronic, but something else will kill you
before this does."

They predict seasons, not weather.
They can't say, "Tomorrow you won't be able to get out
of bed for the pain." So bundle up and wear boots.
They say "That? That's called Photophobia. That's common.
Disorientation? That's common, too; there's medication
for *that,* but sometimes the drugs can inflame
the desire." They can tell you that treatments are unpredictable,
the disease is mysterious, that individuals have unique reactions.
They can't tell you on which day it would be best to stay out
of the kitchen, away from those blades: stainless steel and beckoning.

And they couldn't tell you of this morning's hush, the neat
boundaries: white, black, clean.
Later, it will all turn to mud.
But for the moment, you're laughing,
hard, outloud, alone. The black dog
runs, as fast as the rhythmic spasms of his heart
will allow, pouncing like some other critter
at a fallen mass, as if he might solve the mystery
by smelling it. *Why this one? Why did this piece fall? Why?*
Then he takes off, panting and tired but unable to stop
that impulse—still growing inside, consuming him,
pushing him forward.

ℰℴ

What Are You Looking For?

Katya Uroff

Cynthia puts her hand on my arm. "Honey," she says, "this won't help." She is a petite woman with long, black hair. Many people, when they see her from behind, assume that she is younger than she is. But Cynthia is not young. And neither am I.

I call Andrew in Boston and tell him what I'm going to do. I hear him inhale deeply on a cigarette. Andrew, my youngest son, has been smoking for most of his life. I remember when I found out that he smoked. I was walking around our house and I saw a dump of cigarette butts on the ground right below Andrew's second-floor bedroom window. I ran inside, hopped up the stairs, and went immediately to his room. Andrew was sitting cross-legged on the floor. "Hey Pops," he said to me and, as always, I was initially disarmed by his casualness.

"Andrew," I said, trying to remain steady and authoritarian, "Do you smoke?" I thought he might gulp or look contrite. He was fifteen years old, for God's sakes.

But Andrew had style, had a sense of himself even then. He looked at me and slowly nodded. "Do I ever," he said.

When Andrew hears my plans, he sighs.

"Well," I say, "what do you think?"

I don't know what I expect him to say. Maybe I want his benediction. Maybe I want him to tell me that it is a grand idea, that it is the only idea that makes sense these days, that I am honoring his brother Mark by even thinking of it.

"What exactly," Andrew says instead, "are you looking for?"

"I don't know."

"Then what's the point?"

"I want to retrace his life," I say. "Step by step. I want to go to all the places Mark ever went."

"Yes, but why?"

"I think it's important."

"But there's no need for this. If there's anything you want to know about Mark," Andrew says, "you can ask me."

"No," I say, "that's not what I want."

I don't know how to explain myself, to tell him that I don't want to hear his version of Mark's life. I want to find out on my own, through a series of visits to all the places Mark ever lived, to meet his old friends and colleagues.

We are family. We know too much of the wrong things and too little of what's important. I am certain that Andrew will not be able to tell me what I need to know.

My son, Mark, died last month. He was forty-three years old. He died after a prolonged fight with cancer, a battle that left him feeble, exhausted, forty pounds underweight. I pride myself on the fact that I was there at the end. That means a lot to me. I kept flying back and forth, from Illinois to Atlanta, every weekend until Cynthia suggested that I stay down there for awhile. So I did. For the last five weeks of his life, I was there with him. Which doesn't sound like a long time, I know. But it was. I was in charge of the night shift.

A hospice nurse came in during the day. She'd get him up for awhile so he wouldn't develop bed sores. She'd wash his arms with a wet sponge. She'd light lavender candles in his bedroom when he was sleeping because the scent, she said, was very soothing. Her name was Julie, and I was relieved every day when her shift ended. Her cheerfulness, her efficiency amidst such unbearable sorrow was too much for me. Once she'd leave, after she checked his vital signs one last time, I'd pull up a chair next to Mark's bed and say, "At last!" Mark would nod and smile a little. I would dole out his nighttime pills as if they were candy and he was a young boy again, mouth hanging open, tongue out, waiting for his treat. He couldn't talk very loudly towards the end because the cancer had gotten into his vocal chords, but he'd still try. He'd say something, and I'd pretend to understand. "Oh yes," I'd answer him. "Yes."

One morning, I woke up early to check on him. As I entered his dark bedroom, I could sense that something was different. Mark's breathing had changed slightly, just enough to make me notice. Whereas before he had breathed in and out in a somewhat uniform rhythm, now there were small pauses where his breaths should have been. I crept over to the side of his narrow hospital bed, reached over the bed rail and picked up his hand. His fingers were swollen and his nails had started to turn blue. I said, "OK, OK." I gently patted his hand. I watched the top of his chest move up and down, and then slowly up, and then more slowly down, and then it stopped altogether.

Cynthia still works part-time at a real estate office, but I've been retired from the insurance business for five years now. So I sit at home and think about my son.

Mark and I were never close. At least with Andrew, who was two years younger, I had a kind of repartee. I appreciated Andrew's humor, his joviality. But Mark wasn't like that. He was serious and somber, always kept to himself. One time, he came home during a spring break from college and I found him sitting at the breakfast table, hunched over a bowl of cereal. I sat down next to him, with every intention of asking him about his classes, his friends. But I didn't say a word. He was about nineteen then and had a horrible case of acne all over his cheeks, chin and forehead. His hair needed to be cut. In truth, I barely recognized him; he didn't look like anyone I'd ever know. Not one word came to me to say to my oldest son. Mark ate a few more bites of his cereal then pushed away from the table and left the room.

Things with his mother didn't help. I'd married Barbara right out of college. Mark was born within our first year of marriage. Maybe it was the sudden thrust into parenthood, but Barbara and I never had the kind of marriage that I wanted. She was busy tending to the children, decorating the house, preparing elaborate feasts for neighbors and friends. Here I was, twenty-four years old, presiding over dinner parties with Frank Sinatra in the background and one or both of my sons wailing upstairs. We were still too young to play our parents. I didn't want to come home and see my wife standing in front of the stove with a frilly apron tied neatly around her waist. That wasn't what I wanted.

So there were others, and Barbara found out. She cried and moped and got thinner and thinner, and everyone knew it was my fault. One day she came up to me, her face wet and red with tears, and she said, "As soon as the children get older, I'm leaving you." I didn't believe her, but that's exactly what she did. As soon as Andrew graduated from college, she served me with divorce papers. The word around the neighborhood was that Barbara was finally getting the life that she deserved. No one came by to console me when I moved out.

I met Cynthia six months after the divorce was final. When I told Andrew about her, he said, "A friend of yours is a friend of mine, dear Dad," and even though I knew he was mocking me, he made me laugh. But when I told Mark, he only stared at me. "You'd really like her," I said even though I knew this wasn't true, that he'd be appalled by her dyed hair, her long, painted fingernails, her tight skirts, tall boots. "Oh," Mark said, and nothing else.

But I needed Cynthia. She seemed to understand me when I told her the story of how I had lived my life, what I had done wrong. "Sometimes," she said, "we make the wrong choice."

And then, a few years later, Barbara made a left turn without looking both ways and someone rammed into her side of the car. She was gone right away. After that, no matter what Cynthia said to console me, nothing helped.

First I go to the University of Chicago where Mark received his Ph.D. I live in Danville, a good three hours away from the city, so it's a drive to get there. The engineering department is in an imposing stone building with carved gargoyles peeking out at me over every arched doorway. I walk the wide halls of the building, peering into busy classrooms, until I find the department office. A lady is putting paper into a file cabinet drawer. When she sees me, she slams the drawer shut. I explain that I am Mark Sanders' father and that I'd like to meet Mark's faculty advisor. She sits down at her desk and frowns. "I'm not sure we keep records like that," she says.

"It wasn't that long ago. Fifteen years, give or take. Mark Sanders? Did you know my son?"

She shakes her head. "I started here last month."

I back out of the office slowly and wander the halls again, picturing Mark doing the same. I stop at a window that overlooks a small courtyard. There are still patches of snow on the ground. A green bench tilts to one side. A small, circular bird bath that has been used as an ashtray is next to the bench. This is a dismal view. I wonder if Mark ever stopped here and saw what I'm seeing. I hope not.

The next week I fly to Atlanta to see his office. For the last ten years, Mark was a mechanical engineer at a small firm in one of those suburbs that, not so long ago, was nothing but farmland but is now built up with one-story office buildings, Quik Trips, day care centers, and new churches that resemble hunting lodges. I walk into the reception area and a young girl sitting in front of a computer says: "Sir? Can I help you?"

She leads me to what used to be Mark's office. Someone new has already settled in there. The receptionist curls her hair behind her ear and says, with a question in her voice, "Um, this is Mark's dad?" The man sitting behind the desk jumps up as though I've caught him doing something naughty. He shakes my hand and then quickly leaves. I look around the small, windowless room. Two boxes are stacked on top of one another in the corner of the room. I have no doubt that they are Mark's personal possessions, but I have no interest in going through them. No, I want to stand in his office, where he once stood. That's all.

I asked him once why he chose to be an engineer. It seemed so technical, so precise, such a narrow field. I've sold insurance all my life and I always felt that, with my experience, I could've done anything. But engineering? All that intense education for one purpose only? Mark had looked at me as if I was crazy for asking him that question. Finally he said, "I like to see how things work," and it was my turn to find nothing to say.

When I lean my head back and look up, I see gray ceiling tiles. One block is darker than the others, probably the remnants of some kind of leak. I imagine Mark leaning his head back and seeing the same dreary sight. I wonder what it was like for him. Did he bound into this gloomy room every morning, turn on his computer with its oversized monitor, whistle as he typed line after line of convoluted code? Or was he cautious and careful, as I remembered him? He liked to see how things worked. What did that mean exactly? Why didn't I ask him? Why didn't I say, "Mark, could you explain yourself?"

An overweight young man with a fuzzy growth of beard on his fat cheeks knocks on the open door. I remember seeing him at the funeral but I can't recall his name. This is so unlike me. In my field of business, names are the most important things. That, and a good, firm handshake. And now I can't remember this young man's name.

"Mr. Sanders?"

"Yes?"

"Chip O'Neill."

We shake hands. I want to sit down, but I can't. The only chair available in the office is behind the desk, Mark's old desk, and I won't sit there.

"I heard you were here and I wanted to come and say hello."

"Yes, Chip, thank you."

"We're still reeling from the shock of it."

What do I remember about Chip O'Neill? Did Mark ever mention him?

"Are you OK, Mr. Sanders?"

"Yes, yes. Chip, let me ask you, were you my son's friend?"

Chip clears his throat. He cups his fingers into a small fist and places it over his mouth to cough delicately. "I'd like to think of myself that way. Yes."

"Did Mark like coming to work every day?"

"I'm sorry?"

"Did he enjoy coming to work every day?"

"He was an excellent engineer. Really top-rate."

"That's not what I'm asking."

Chip pauses. "Mark seemed happy here, Mr. Sanders. If that's what you want to know."

I realize that I'm not going to get anything from Chip O'Neill. He is a fat, young man who doesn't know anything about death, about dying, about choices. I wave my hand in the air and turn away, pretending that some posting on a small cork bulletin board has interested me. I want Chip to leave.

Chip touches my arm as I read a sentence from a clipping about the latest motion sensor technology. "He got promoted right before he got sick," Chip says. "He didn't want to do anything to celebrate, but I made him. We went to Ruby Tuesday's, not too far from here. We sat at the bar and had a beer. I thought we were having a good time, but I'll never forget this: I slapped him on the back and said, 'You did it!' and Mark just muttered, 'Finally, finally, finally.'"

I don't turn around. I let Chip O'Neill's story settle into me, like a deep, cold air penetrating my skin. Chip sighs and then leaves the office but I'm barely aware that he's gone. I'm too busy imagining, no, feeling the bitterness that my son felt as he sipped his congratulatory beer. He was promoted, yes, but it had taken a long time, too long, and that knowledge leached the joy out of it. I know all about that.

When I was starting out, there were two of us in the home office who were the young bucks, the up and coming stars. Freddie Johnson and I were good friends. We'd go out after work, boast of our accomplishments to each other. We were the future of the company. One night we were at a bar and a woman slid into our booth with her drink, as if she had known us all her life. Her name was Marianne, and I went to her apartment that night instead of going home. Freddie watched us leave together. He actually slapped me on the back and said, "Be good now." He had a wife and two children, like me, but he never seemed tempted by anything. But how could I resist Marianne? That's what I asked myself that night: how could I resist her?

The next morning I came into work a little late, and they had already announced Freddie's promotion. Freddie was beaming. His face turned red when he saw me, but he didn't stop smiling. He was the one who was going places. Not me.

Our friendship ended after that. There were even a few years, more than a few, when Freddie was my boss. He gave me performance reviews. He decided on my raises.

I leave Mark's office and drive to his ex-wife's house. Kim lives in another suburb, north of Atlanta. I turn onto a wide, deserted street. No cars are parked in driveways. No one is out, pushing a stroller or holding a toddler's hand while walking, even though it is a pleasant enough day. I drive past a swimming pool, covered with blue tarp for the winter months, and an imposing club house. All the houses have identical, grand palladium windows above their front doors. In Kim's front yard, three Bradford pear trees—slender, frail trunks and wispy branches—struggle to flourish.

Kim and Mark knew each other for years before getting married. Everyone thought they'd be together forever, but they didn't last much after their son Bradley was born.

I park in front of her house and get out of the car. I plan on walking around the neighborhood, getting a feel for it, imagining what it would be like to live in a place like this—so quiet, so bland, every house a mirror of the next.

Then Kim opens the front door. "Hello?" She calls out.

She leads me into the living room. The last time I was in this house was five years ago, when Bradley was born. It's been redecorated since. Everything is a variation of peach—the color of the walls, the soft couch that I sink into, the long, heavy draperies that cover each window.

"I wasn't expecting to see you," I say.

"I'm waiting for Bradley to come home."

"Come home?"

"From school. He's in kindergarten."

"Right," I say, "I knew that."

Kim sits down on an ottoman. She leans forward. I think she's going to say something, but then it's clear that she's not, that she's waiting for me to speak.

"I'm retracing Mark's life," I begin and she leans back.

"Yes," she says, "Andrew told me."

I didn't know that Kim and Andrew talk. Were they ever close? I don't know. I don't remember ever seeing them together. At the funeral, Kim kept her distance from the rest of us. She came by herself, without Bradley. First she said that Bradley was sick with a cold. Then she said that she didn't want Bradley remembering this.

"Well," I say, "I'm catching a flight out later today. I'm going to Myrtle Beach where we vacationed every year as a family. Did Mark ever tell you about Myrtle Beach?"

Kim frowns. "Of course he did."

"I remember that he used to go crab fishing there. I think I can probably find the pier he used. It was always one particular one, from what I remember. He said it was his lucky spot. Then I think I'll go back to Illinois and drive over to Indianapolis. Do you remember that he taught school there for a year or so before he went to graduate school? He taught math, I believe."

Kim nods. "He didn't like that job very much. He didn't like teaching," she says.

"No?"

"No."

"Well, still…"

She flicks something off her eyelash with the side of her finger. "I don't know why you're doing this."

I don't answer her.

She stands up. "He's gone. He's not here anymore," she says. "You can't get him back."

"It's a mean and horrible thing," I say, "to outlive your child."

"But how is any of this going to help?"

"I want to know my son."

She stares down and her forehead has a deep line creasing it, splitting it down the middle. Her hands are clenched into fists and, for a second, she reminds me of Barbara. I remember how angry I made Barbara, how I disappointed her in some basic way, and it wasn't only the infidelity. It was everything else, too.

It was my forgetfulness around the house, how I'd say I'd get to the leaves or replace a light bulb, but I'd never do it. It was my reluctance with Mark, how Barbara begged me to teach him things, things that Andrew took to naturally, like how to throw a ball, how to use a mitt.

"Do you really want to know him?" Kim asks, her voice rising.

"Yes, of course." I stand up to face her, but I can barely choke out the words.

"When we decided to divorce," she says, "he got down on his knees and cried into his hands. 'One more chance,' he said. It was so unusual for him, all that emotion. I was shocked, and just watched him cry and beg. Then he got up off the floor and that was it." She unclenches her hands, her fingers spread out for a second, and then curls them into fists again. "So now he's gone and sometimes I think about what would've happened if I had said, 'Yes, let's give it one more chance.'"

I see my son, knees hard against the wood floor, hands clutched together as if in prayer. When he told me about his divorce, he had been so calm and matter of fact. "Kim and I have agreed," he told me on the phone, "to live apart for the time being."

"But the thing is—he wasn't really like that," Kim continues, "That was the only time. Otherwise he was pretty detached, cold. Sometimes I'd reach out to hug him or even to touch him, and he'd flinch."

She moves past me and starts straightening some throw pillows on the couch. I watch her fuss with the furniture and then she turns around again. "You want to do something?" she asks, and now her voice is suddenly stronger, harsher. "Be a grandfather to Bradley. Visit him. Call him. Send him toys, letters. That's something you can do. At least stay now until he gets home."

I need to get out of here, make my way back to the airport. I need to go to the beach where there are sandy beach roads and old, rickety piers. I need to find that school in Indianapolis and walk among students—children I don't know.

"I can't," I say. I try to smile but my lips are trembling. Bradley has dark brown hair and black eyes and I remember that there's something about him—the shape of his face, the curve of his lips—that looks so much like Mark it's almost cruel.

"It's not that I don't love Bradley. I do," I say, hoping she'll understand because I can't tell her the truth—how I never told Mark how proud I was of him, how I never said 'good job,' not even while he was dying, when he was so weak he could barely sit up in bed, yet he'd struggle anyway, inching himself up on his elbows, chin jutting forward, every muscle in his forearms straining. I didn't do it because I was afraid to, afraid that he'd somehow uncover a hidden energy and accuse me in his last, clear voice, of being a fraud, of playing the part of the devoted father, when everyone had always known, and who more than Mark, that I had been no-good, absent and self-absorbed.

You get to a certain age and you can't fool yourself anymore. Bradley doesn't need someone like me in his life.

Kim strides to the front door and jerks it open. "Go," she says. Her voice is flat.

"Please," I say.

"Just go," she says.

I make my way to the car. My head feels heavy and light at the same time and it takes all the strength I have to move. I'm opening the car door when I hear Kim running toward me. She has something in her hand. I take it from her but I don't look at it. Instead, I look at her. She is crying.

"Here," she says, "This is for you. Mark left it when he moved out. I always meant to give it back to him but I never did. And he never asked for it."

With my free hand, I reach for her. Before I know what I'm doing, I find myself touching her cheek with my fingertips. She has such smooth skin. I touch her tears. She steps back.

"I don't know why I'm doing this. You don't deserve it. I guess I feel sorry for you. For all of us."

She turns around and walks back inside her house. I am left standing next to the rental car on this empty street, with something in the palm of my hand. I draw my hand closer and see the back of a photograph. Before I flip it over, I imagine what it is. An old picture of Mark as a toddler, frowning as he sits in the sandbox we used to have in the back yard of our first home? Could it be a picture of Mark in his Cub Scout uniform, solemnly holding up his fingers in the proper salute?

Or is it something worse? Is it a picture of our family—Barbara and me standing behind our two boys? Although her head would be tilted slightly towards me, I'd be staring straight ahead at the camera, with an insincere smile. My hands would rest lightly on my sons' shoulders, only because I didn't want to wrap my arms around Barbara's waist. My boys would look as if they wanted to flee, go, be anywhere else instead of posing with their family. A smirk from Andrew, a sullen frown from Mark. Our family—as it was, as everyone knew it to be.

What picture did Mark keep? I'm afraid to see what it is. I want to find out more about my son but I can't bear any more sadness. I climb into the car, leaving the picture face down on the passenger side seat next to me. I am ashamed of myself, of my irrational fear of this inanimate object. I stare at its small, square shape and for a moment it seems like a viper snake, coiled and ready to strike.

This is ridiculous, I tell myself. I am a grown man. I am on a journey. I want, I *need*, to find out more about my son. I need to do this for Mark. I wordlessly repeat this steady beat of words—for Mark, for Mark, for Mark—until I have the strength to pick up the picture and turn it over. With shaky fingers, I bring it closer to my face.

It is a picture of a young man. He is wearing a button down shirt with the sleeves rolled up and his tie is long and crooked. His dark hair is very short, cropped close to his head. He is lean but his arms are strong, as he lifts a small baby up in the air. The baby is laughing. One of his sun suit straps has slipped off his plump shoulder. The young man is smiling at this baby and he looks happy, gloriously happy, as if everything that ever meant anything to him has suddenly appeared. It is me. It is my son. ಠ

Joy

Margaret A. Robinson

that it's Wednesday, the work week's tallest finger,
the hand's mountain peak

that soon I'll walk with my friend, striding down hills,
struggling up

that he still has one lung, I still have one breast, we may
see a hawk

for the clear back yard sky, holding only two clouds,
now drifting off

for bare trees and thin shadows stretched to gigantic length

for Longfellow forests

for villanelles and free verse

for leftovers to carry for lunch, take-out Szechuan
broccoli and rice

that at work I can make students laugh

that chickadees visit the feeder

for having no child in Iraq

&

Walking the Labyrinth:
A Landscape of Grief

Carolyn Megan

It begins on a clear winter morning in early January, after Meg has come back from a run. While eating breakfast with her son, Michael, she is no longer able to speak. Later she'll describe it as forming thoughts in her head but not being able to find words and sentences. Michael becomes annoyed at first, angry that she isn't making sense and responding to his questions.

It begins here: my brother Tom driving his wife Meg to the hospital, Meg being airlifted to Boston because of fear that she has suffered a cerebral aneurysm. But no, it's not an aneurysm. It blossoms into a hemorrhaged tumor, bleeding out and impeding speech. She has surgery to remove the tumor and awaits the biopsy result. All spring Meg moves into the language of cancer.

All spring, we move into the slow unwinding of language.

There is the desire to embrace the magic of certain words: trials, percentages, benign, remission. But there is no fixed vocabulary here, no vowel that doesn't harden to a consonant; no consonant that doesn't slip into a vowel. Language shifts into a landscape of tidal pools and currents. First aneurysm, then brain tumor, then cancer, then melanoma, then metastasized melanoma. Each word or phrase becomes a moment, a fixed point, and then, just as quickly, erodes into another. We are at a loss for words and avoid, for now, the ultimate naming: death. We hold out hope and cling to the language's shift. We barter, we accommodate.

Each step is a negotiation not only with language but also with memory and time. The desire is to name the present without it becoming lost to interpretation, and to imagine how it will be reflected upon weeks, months, years from now. And yet, the very nature of a shifting landscape, a shifting language, means a constant negotiation with time, with flux. Words become loose and flabby, even though they have a concrete sound. Shadings on an MRI one week become lesions the following week; lesions become tumors, and the following month, who knows? There is an unsteadiness and a distrust of words, knowing how they loose themselves and change shape and form so quickly. They multiply like the cancer cells in Meg's body, reproducing at alarming rates. We speak carefully, choose words carefully; we don't trust their meanings; we look for the nuances: spot, lesion, tumor, soft tissue, brain.

Writing, I tell my students, allows us to place ourselves in a moment in time, naming our unique response to the world. Yet, with Meg's illness, the story on page is unsatisfying: too contrived, yet not contrived enough. I look for the form that can name where she is now, without erasure. I flounder and doubt myself, doubt the word. We are, and Meg is, an unfolding story which resists narrative and plot. My sister says it's like we're on a conveyor belt but don't know where we're going. So we fall back on imagery, stories of other people's fight with cancer. Five different people have given Tom and Meg copies of Lance Armstrong's cancer memoir.

The truth is, Meg's cancer does have a plot. It's easy for me to go online to read the course of melanoma. I have an ear for it now, but I wrestle with telling *her* story. I live and write in a form of arbitrage—relating details of the present in terms of how I will look back on it from the future. I'm not comfortable with waiting to see how the story unfolds. And this failure of words, failure of imagination, seems like a betrayal.

At the start of summer, a series of labyrinths begin to appear on the beach near where I live. Just after high tide, when the water pulls back, leaving the beach a smooth palate of hard sand, the labyrinths appear perfectly etched into the thin silt of the sand's surface. At first, the labyrinth is rendered in small scale, and then a second time, the same labyrinth appears in grand scale, so that several people can wind their way through it at once.

Each day, I mark the tide charts and walk the beach hoping for the labyrinths' maker to appear. Through June into July, along with the sound of radio music, seagulls, dogs barking, Frisbee throwers, body surfers, there is the quiet movement of people winding their way through the labyrinth, their shoulders sometimes touching.

I, too, walk the labyrinths, cocooning my way into the center, winding on a path that neighbors the center point and then, surprisingly, at the next turn, winds out to the periphery. Like breath, the labyrinths draw in and expand at the same time. With each tide, they disappear. They suggest a still and fixed point in time in the constant ebb and flow of tide. I walk the arcing path with the knowledge that the next tide will wash the labyrinth, my footprints, and those of others, away. The labyrinths become a walking meditation of the present.

It's February, one month after her diagnosis, and Meg is in the hospital for testing. I sit with my niece Laurel as she plays a video game. She is eight years old, a soccer fanatic who wears her soccer uniform almost every day, her long blond braids falling below her shoulders. She knows about her mother's tumor and the surgery to have it removed, but does not yet know of the cancer diagnosis. But clearly she *knows*. People come by to drop off food. They speak quietly at the door so that Laurel and her brother can't hear, though Michael tells me later that he learned they would have to move, learned that his mother would be going into the hospital, by listening to these hushed conversations.

On the computer screen, a turtle wearing a small backpack is winding along a troubled path of obstacles and falling objects. As one road disintegrates below him, a bridge suddenly appears and, with a flick of her wrist, Laurel sends the turtle jumping to safety. "So what's the object?" I ask Laurel.

"The turtle's looking for her parents and can't find them," she answers, staring intently at the screen. "They may be at the doctor's; they may be even dead. I'm trying to find them." The turtle jumps from bridge to falling bridge and Laurel moves the turtle calmly with the tap of her fingers on the keyboard. The clock in the right-hand corner counts down how much time she has and I'm ready to grab the keyboard and find the turtle's parents myself. I want to manipulate her story, give her hope for a different outcome. When the turtle jumps into the void, its image melts; 'Game Over' flashes on screen. Laurel pushes back from her computer, "See, still can't find them. The turtle never finds them."

April: it's the simpler moments that fill me with grief, and leave me at a loss to write. The ground has finally let loose of winter and the fields have settled into a thick mud. It's been a long, hard winter of doctor appointments, tests, biopsies, and diagnoses. Outside, the scent of dogwood and magnolia startle the air. Laurel runs across the field and I follow in pursuit with their dog, Aran. Her braids swooshing against her back, Laurel is as light and loose-limbed as the spring breeze softening the air. Laurel spots two hawks circling and we run to stay under them as if they are harbingers of spring and summer. *Or truth tellers,* I think. *Let us know what you see.*

I am caught—already in the future and looking back on the present, trying to form a narrative. If Meg survives, this is a moment of hope: the hawks, a sign of good things to come. If she dies, this is a moment of innocence for Laurel, before the truth rushes in and she is left motherless. It is this arbitrage of the future, here in the present, that silences me, hinders my language, stops the story. The sky darkens, thin clouds stretch on the horizon. Laurel and I are caught in the gloaming—between day and night, winter and spring—and two red-tailed hawks circling above.

Labyrinths were initially designed for pilgrimages. Unlike a maze, which offers several turns possibly leading to dead ends, the labyrinth is a fixed path mapped out for the walker. It is a matter of submitting to the labyrinth's structure and discipline, and setting an intention. Like life, the labyrinth only asks that you let it take you where it goes. There are five paths or intentions for walking the labyrinth: Path of Memory, Path of Questioning, Path of Silence, Path of Image, Path of Prayer.

All summer the labyrinths allowed for a specific sort of stillness, marking and fixing a moment, like the writer delineating a moment on page. All summer the labyrinths became an opportunity to hold the path of Meg's journey while knowing that by its very nature, it would be erased again by surging tides or new language.

Path of Memory

Meg remembers having a mole removed from her arm in the 80s. The growth was benign but now she wonders.

On my refrigerator, there is a photo of Tom and Meg from a vacation one year ago. Meg smiles to the camera. Her left eye squints from the glare of the summer sun. I wonder, looking at the photo, was that the beginning, even then, of a mass of abnormal cells pressing against her brain?

Tom tells me that fifteen years ago, when he and Meg first moved into the private school where Meg teaches, they walked the campus late one night, sat in a grove of trees and looked up at the moon. It was a hopeful time, he says. Thinking of their new life there, how long they might stay, the family they might have. I look back on that now, he says, and can't believe the circumstances that now have us leaving the school.

It's a trick of memory, the desire of language to name and to complete the story. We have no experience or memory to guide us now, so we create memory, we revise. We reread the past to understand how we arrived at the present. We want to accommodate to the present by finding its roots in this path of memory.

Path of Questioning

"Why is this happening to us?" Michael asks Tom. In the course of the last year, Tom has been in the hospital for several weeks as a result of a sledding accident, Michael has suffered two seizures, and now Meg has been diagnosed with cancer. "Why do all these bad things happen to us and no one else?" Michael asks.

Laurel is sitting in the back seat of her grandfather's car with her cousin. They are laughing about the soda they are drinking, making faces to one another, when out of the blue, Laurel asks, "Grampa, is my mother going to die?"

Path of Silence

Meg has been in the hospital for a week of Interleukin-2 therapy. In a phone conversation, Tom says, "There is no language for this." But we learn. By the end of the first morning of Meg's treatment, we refer to Interleukin as IL-2; we are fast learners.

The truth is that language does develop, even if through default. Perhaps this is what is most striking, and sad. And it is nowhere clearer than talking with Laurel and Michael.

In January, when Tom first tells them that Meg is sick and needs to have an operation on her brain to make her better, Laurel and Michael laugh and ask if Meg will go bald.

In March, once the kids learn that Meg has cancer, Michael asks, "Is it the good kind or the bad kind?" Laurel begins to use the cancer as a reference point. "Was that before or after my Mom got cancer?"

In July, when Meg begins the intensive IL-2 treatments, I ask Michael if he is worried about his mom. "No," he responds. "It's not like she's dying or anything."

"Oh," a friend says to me later when I tell her this story. "He knows that she's dying." Somewhere in his thoughts, Michael works the narrative, taking on the possibility of what is to come, but first there is this place of 'silence' where he begins to take on the various layers of realization.

Studies of learners of second languages identify a period of silence that occurs naturally during language acquisition. During this time, the students stop talking while the brain's circuitry absorbs the new sounds and formulations in preparation to enter the language.

It's not that there is a lack of language; we are only in a place of silence, a place of pause.

Path of Image

In the x-ray, Meg's skull appears as light gray and the tumor as a knob of white. Tom asked me to hold onto the x-rays months ago. They sit behind one of the bookcases in my study waiting to be rediscovered the next time I move or rearrange the room. Already they represent the past, when Meg's narrative was that only of a tumor and surviving the seepage of blood across her brain's surface.

Eventually the narrative will take over on its own and steer the course, creating a final image. But in January, it was only one ghostly knob, dense and round, hovering in the brain's gray matter.

February: it's one of the oncologists who offers the image; he tells Tom and Meg that melanoma is like dandelions. "We can pluck it, but after awhile it starts popping up everywhere." At first, the image is only an idea; it burns in the way that the desire for spring burns in late February, when winter feels long and tired. But when I drive down a country road that spring and look out over a landscape of yellow dandelions, it comes as a shock, this beautiful and also horrifically apt image. Melanoma seeding its way through Meg's body.

Even in their impermanence, the beach labyrinths provide the promise of balance: a point of arrival, a point of departure, a sure route. They are never the same from day to day and yet become a way to mark and note daily change. Like pen on page, to walk them again and again is to understand points of arrival and points of departure.

Path of Prayer

I'll miss. I'll miss. I'll miss.

By May the kids know that Meg has cancer. During a visit, Laurel shows me a story she has written entitled simply "Things I'll miss about Aran." The story consists of a list of the things that Laurel will miss about her dog Aran when he dies. *I'll miss you sticking your big snout into the trash. I'll miss you bringing snakes and animals to the house. I'll miss sleeping with you. I'll miss your begging food from me at the table.* The list becomes incantatory, an offering to an unknown future where Aran, now a healthy two-year-old lab, no longer exists. Laurel reads the story to me a second time, repeating over and over the prayer she is only beginning to understand. *"I'll miss. I'll miss. I'll miss."*

"Eat my bed." I'm not sure of its origins; Laurel just stumbled upon the line and she and Michael say it back to one another, sometimes as an insult, sometimes as a joke. It is a powerful prayer, able to cut stories to the close, able to reduce Laurel to the floor laughing hard and long. *"Eat my bed."*

In June, when Meg is in the hospital for an MRI, Laurel asks for story after story of her father, of Michael, of herself. One night, Laurel tells me a story of a ski trip 'before Mom had cancer' when she, Michael, her father and mother all fell down while crossing a slippery patch of ice.

Michael interrupts. "Actually Laurel that's not true. I didn't fall down."

Laurel becomes frustrated. "Okay. Fine. But Mom and Dad and I did."

Michael interrupts again. "No, Dad didn't either."

"Michael," she says, "stop interrupting."

He continues, "Actually, Laurel. No one fell. You fell and you took Mom down with you." There's a pause, and I'm aware Laurel might begin to cry or yell at Michael; feelings are close to the surface when Meg is in the hospital. Laurel's face draws a surprised blank as though she might cry, and then she starts laughing. She falls to the floor, gripping her stomach, laughing so hard, it sounds like a prayer or chant. Michael too, happy to have made her laugh, lets out his freer boyhood laugh. "Hey, Laurel," he says. *"Eat my bed."*

We make stories to provide hope, but also need to tell the stories of loss of hope. We cling to language; cling to images. And in the end, we rely on the story and language to move us through.

We are continually in search of the image to name the huge and unpredictable. It is a hypnotic, unimaginably long and short journey. We aren't using a new language, really. It's the same old story of suffering, of celebrating, of readying ourselves to shed this world as we know it. Whether it's a childhood world where mother and father are healthy and safe, or one where we grow into old age with our partners and die peacefully, each of us sheds story after story, narrative after narrative, looking for and creating the form to name where and who we are.

"Cancer is in our lives now," Tom says to me. "I've already lost the Meg that I knew."

On a Monday evening in early July, I walk with Michael and Laurel to the church parking lot across from where they live, to play Wiffle ball. "You're on everyone's team," Michael says. "You're the automatic pitcher and fielder for me and Laurel." I toss loping pitches to where Michael and then Laurel stand gripping the plastic yellow bat. When Michael hits the ball, it makes a satisfying smack and floats up out of the range of the streetlights and then comes back down from the darkness. When we get bored, we run relay races from one parking spot to the next. Then we sit on the curb and watch the moths float up towards the parking lot lights. Laurel sits on my lap and I run my hand through her sweaty, tangled strands. On a nearby street, an ice cream truck plays a tinny *Pop Goes the Weasel*. The moon rises; the day seems endless.

"Can we get an ice cream if the truck comes here?" Laurel asks.

Michael stretches out on the asphalt, resting his head against the Wiffle bat. "I'm so glad that we don't have to do any homework," Michael says.

It occurs to me that Michael and Laurel are truly my teachers of how to walk the impermanence of the labyrinth, for they seem able to inhabit each moment, each feeling fully.

It's at night when thoughts of Meg's cancer will creep in and take hold. Meg is in the hospital for another IL-2 treatment but the doctor has accidentally punctured her lung while trying to establish the port. A tube threads into her collapsed lung and Tom sits by her side. I'll lie with Laurel initially; she pulls my arm over her as she rolls onto her side of the bed and then clasps her hand tightly into mine. I'll wait until I hear the slow steady rise and fall of her breath. Then I'll move into Michael's room, where he plays with his Game Boy. He is older, the cusp of puberty. "Do you want some company while you go to sleep?" "Sure," he says, as if he is doing me a favor. In the dark, Michael rambles on in long narratives about soccer players, friends, the Red Sox. Finally I'll say he can't talk anymore and that it's time to sleep. I'll ask him if he wants me to rub his back and he flips over to his stomach, slowly relaxes.

Out on the beach near my home, the tide pounds against the shore, spewing seaweed and caught pieces of driftwood. Later, someone, a spirit or person, will make her way down to the shoreline and draw a new labyrinth. ◊

The Next Week

Joan Michelson

The next week vanished, though there
were days and each asked something

beyond mourning with the mirrors
covered, since nothing was prepared.

On Monday you were autopsied.
On Tuesday booked for burial

in a double-plot we bought
in Enfield. On Wednesday the search

for clothes to wear and answering
the phone. Thursday, half-past three,

the ceremony. Then we tried
to cover up your coffin using

one shovel made of iron
and our hands. Was there a Friday?

On Friday you were one week dead.
I remember warmth on Sunday.

My sister packed her bag, then walked
with us through Highgate to the Heath.

&

First Anniversary

Joan Michelson

I have to fight your death. Already a year
nearly. All this month of darkening, nearly
never-ending, a year. Nearly a year
of battle lost, this other year we took

no holiday, again went nowhere. Next week
I see you hand-to-mouth in mocking gasp
at my leg stuck in plaster,—you, in the glass
behind the house plants, watching how I hop.

After a year, my ankle merely swells.
A year like no year; and you again nearly,
last night in the window looking well.
Incredible, poised to win. *Well stop!*

I say, *A truce until I'm cold, out, down
beside you, nearly victor, nearly gone.*

୫

Breathing

Cortney Davis

Sometime during the eerie, disorganized half-hour before midnight, Peter Locke, a medical intern, arrived to see James Harris, his eighty-four-year old patient, whose condition was rapidly deteriorating. The patient's private duty nurse, Irene, had paged Peter just as he was hurrying toward his dreary, cell-like call room, hoping to catch a few moments of sleep before the next wave of admissions from the ER started rolling in. His head ached, his stomach felt vaguely upset—perhaps it was the hasty dinner of French fries and a greasy cheeseburger—and he didn't have any idea what he could possibly do to help Mr. Harris. Peter had admitted this patient ten days before—just two weeks into internship. He saw Mr. Harris every day on rounds and even tried to cram in some reading about end-of-life care and the importance of doctor-patient bonding during a terminal illness. But now, as Peter's first rotation of internship was about to end, he was, frankly, tapped out.   Part of him hoped that Mr. Harris would die quietly and agreeably during the night, when some other intern was on call, but now it seemed that he might have to be the one to pronounce Mr. Harris after all. He would be the one to pretend, in front of a grieving family, to listen for the heart beat that he already knew wouldn't be there, to shine his penlight into the dead man's fixed, pinpoint pupils, then turn away from the body and say the words his chief resident had drilled into him, words he had yet to actually say aloud: *I'm sorry. Your (insert here grandfather, grandmother, father, mother, husband, wife, son, daughter, companion, friend) is gone. Please let us know if we can be of any help.*

Peter wondered about the implications of the word, *gone*. Couldn't he simply say *dead*, which seemed more truthful, more final? And why not ask if there was something *he* could do, rather than something *we* could do? Was that purposeful evasion meant to derail any possible requests, to keep the family at arm's length just when they might have innumerable needs and questions? This avoidance of precise, personal words suggested to Peter that the bonding he read about wasn't, after all, such a good idea. A patient who'd been pronounced gone instead of dead might sneak back, reappearing unexpectedly, just when everyone had been convinced of his absence. Such incongruities floated into Peter's mind when he was particularly tired, when the mountain of technical information he tried to digest was overwhelming, giving him heartburn more profound than anything caused by cheeseburgers and fries.

Entering room 23B, anticipating Mr. Harris's demise, Peter felt mortally fragile himself, as if his skin had peeled away to expose the network of nerves beneath. If there was one more attack, if a nurse chided him, accused him, or demanded of him one more thing he couldn't do, Peter thought he might just explode. If Mr. Harris were dead, lying there as inert and vulnerable as the cadaver Peter had dissected in the anatomy lab years earlier, Peter knew he was in danger of crying, something he hadn't allowed himself to do in four years of college, four years of medical school, and three and a half weeks of internship.

Mrs. Irene McNamara stood up when Peter entered and walked part way across the room to greet him.

"Dr. Locke? I'm Irene." She looked, Peter thought, fifty-ish, maybe less, with reddish hair tinged with gray, and light eyes that were framed by fine crow's feet when she smiled. Good, Peter thought. She's smiling. Mr. Harris isn't dead—a crude thought, but he didn't regret it. Knowing the patient was alive gave him a feeling of relief. He smiled back.

"I didn't know they made private duty nurses anymore," Peter said.

"Cherry Ames, Private Duty Nurse," Irene said. "Once upon a time one of my favorite books."

Irene looked, Peter thought, both kind and tired, nevertheless crisp in her patterned scrubs and white nurses' shoes. Standing next to her, he felt rumpled and sweaty. He turned to look at Mr. Harris. A day or so before the patient had been in a semi-private room, bloated and noisily in pain, yelping every time a nurse touched him. Even when no one was prodding him, Mr. Harris would groan with each breath, annoying his roommate, who complained to the head nurse. Peter had ordered Mr. Harris moved to a private room, a dying room, although no one called it that. Seeing their father alone in a room far away from the wards and also from the nurse's station, Mr. Harris's daughters worried. Supposing he called for help? What if the nurses didn't hear, and he died alone? Peter agreed with the daughters' request for a private duty nurse, and the nursing office assigned Irene McNamara.

Mr. Harris was lying on his back in the middle of the narrow hospital bed. His hip bones, like two shark fins, tented up the white sheet and green thermal blanket draped over him. His mouth was open, the red, dry ridges of his hard palate visible, his forehead waxy with sweat. Peter looked back at Irene.

"He's actively dying," she said, matter-of-factly, as she shifted Mr. Harris's pillow. "Sometimes this phase can take hours. Or days." The activity of her body, as she moved around Mr. Harris's bed, tucking and soothing him, seemed almost incongruous in this room of death.

"I haven't seen you here before," Peter replied. "Maybe I haven't been on call the nights you've been here."

Irene moved to the other end of the bed and adjusted Mr. Harris's feet. She nodded as she worked. "Of course I read your notes on the chart."

"Glad to hear someone does," Peter said, stuffing loose papers back into his clipboard. "Usually the nurses don't pay much attention to an intern's notes."

Irene murmured slightly in response but didn't look up at Peter. "I'm concerned that my patient's pain control isn't adequate. I'd like you to increase his morphine. And I wonder if you'd take a look at that one spot on his hip that's breaking down. I just can't seem to—"

"How much morphine is he getting now?" Peter interrupted, his voice sharper than he'd meant it to be.

Irene picked up the flow sheet and handed it to Peter. She had written each time she had pushed a few milligrams of morphine into Mr. Harris's IV. Next to each dose were numbers indicating his blood pressure and his respirations, both of which were steadily dropping. His last blood pressure had been 70/40. His respirations, though they were noisy and deep, were now only eight per minute. A few times, Peter saw, the respirations had shot up to 25 or 30 a minute. Irene's notations indicated that shortly after the morphine was delivered, the breathing had slowed. All this he'd have known, had he stopped to check Mr. Harris's chart before coming in. Handing the sheet back to Irene, he felt foolish.

How he hated being among the dying! He couldn't stand to look at Mr. Harris, not because he lacked empathy or pity, but because he was tired and cranky, and he'd rather be doing something instead of simply standing around and watching. Still, he felt no desire to leave the room. Here, at least, there were no alarm bells or chief residents barking orders, no nurses laughing in the hallway or calling him at three a.m., just when he had fallen asleep, for an aspirin order.

"My grandfather died at home when I was ten," Peter said, the words surprising him, coming as they did from a distant memory. "I'm not sure what he died of. I can't remember much about him, only what my mother tells me."

Mr. Harris suddenly reminded him a bit of his grandfather. Something about the thin mouth or the ears, the fleshy lobes. When Peter first met Mr. Harris, the chief resident had stood back and motioned Peter forward to the semi-conscious old man's bedside. "Okay, Sherlock Holmes," the resident said. "Go ahead and examine Mr. Harris. He's got a fascinating murmur. Makes you think his heart should kill him, but it'll probably be pneumonia. He had a small rectal carcinoma, got a stroke after the colostomy. Now a hospital-acquired pneumonia." Peter had examined Mr. Harris while the resident scribbled in the chart.

This time, it was Irene standing guard as Peter unraveled his stethoscope, wearily pushed up Mr. Harris's gown and listened, for the twentieth time this week, to the muffled lub-dub of his heart. Then Peter pressed the stethoscope tight against the chest and listened as the patient's raspy breaths came in fits and starts. He tucked the stethoscope under Mr. Harris's back. "The poor guy's drowning," he said. Listening, Peter felt a little short of breath himself.

Irene slipped on latex gloves and wiped inside Mr. Harris's mouth with a glycerin swab. The swab came out glistening, loops of mucus hanging from it, like strands of lights strung along holiday roof tops. Peter's stomach turned.

"Yes," said Irene. "I know. Anything we can give him to dry up these secretions?"

Peter looked away, pretending to study the IV bag and the plastic tubing, all the familiar, clean equipment surrounding the bed. The acid burning a hole in his stomach felt like fire. He expected to see, any minute now, a puff of smoke rise from his scrubs, followed by a flame that would leap out, igniting his lab coat. Maybe the nurse would come to his rescue, throwing a glass of water on him or wrapping him in a blanket. Maybe she would tell him what medications helped to dry up secretions. Maybe he would push Mr. Harris over the edge of the bed, disposing of him so he could lie down himself and go to sleep, while Irene watched over him, checking his blood pressure every so often to make sure he was still alive. Peter said, "I'll up the morphine."

Irene tied the patient's gown. "And for the secretions?" She folded the blanket under Mr. Harris's chin and readjusted the nasal oxygen.

Peter sighed. Suddenly a part of him wanted to bolt from the room. Another part of him felt pity for Mr. Harris, a rush of empathy that surprised him.

"Why don't we turn off the IV," Irene said, blotting Mr. Harris's forehead with a washcloth. "He doesn't really need the fluids now, does he?"

Peter flipped the pages of his clipboard. "Sure. D/C the IV fluids." His stomach churned.

"And before you leave," Irene said, "can you help me give him a boost up?"

Peter looked at her.

"Just go around to the other side, and we'll hoist him up a bit. He's sliding."

Irene motioned Peter to the other side of the bed, which had been raised up almost waist high. "Just hook your arm under his and grab the draw sheet." She positioned her body on Mr. Harris's left. "On the count of three, hoist him up, but make sure you pull the draw sheet at the same time."

Peter put his clipboard on the bedside table and leaned over Mr. Harris's right side. Together at her count of three, their heads almost touching, Irene and Peter hauled Mr. Harris up toward the head of the bed like two farmers heaving a bale of hay off the tailgate of a truck. Then they both stood. Irene rubbed the small of her back with both hands. Peter grabbed his clipboard and held it tight under one arm.

"So, you're on call tonight," Irene said.

"Yes. My luck." Peter shoved his other hand into his lab coat pocket. His arms were too long, his frame too tall, his knees too knobby, his short hair too unruly. Every part of him seemed ill at ease and out of place. He wondered if the nurse was married, if she had children. She could be my mother, he thought, and that realization both unsettled and intrigued him. He wondered where she lived and what she did when she wasn't at the hospital, as he sometimes tried to imagine his patients' private lives. He hugged the clipboard until its hard surface pressed against the buttons of his white coat.

"Do you think he'll die tonight?" he asked. "I've never pronounced anyone before."

"What'll happen is just when you're finally asleep, I'll call to wake you up," Irene said, without a trace of irony in her voice. "Then you can call your resident, so he won't get any sleep either."

Peter wanted to protest that he wasn't worried about sleep, he was worried about death. About how it would be to stand alone in the room in death's presence, to touch its cold skin and rest his warm hands upon its sunken chest. Instead he said, a bit too loudly, "Call me if you need me, okay?" and walked out of the room.

At two a.m., Peter Locke poked his head back into room 23B. Irene had balanced Mr. Harris on his left side. The sheets were pulled down and she was washing his back. Mr. Harris's breathing was hoarse but audible. "He's still with us?" Peter asked.

Irene looked up. "And you? You're still awake?"

"I had to admit an elderly woman with a fever. Frankly, she looks as bad as Mr. Harris. I thought maybe I could swing by before I tried to catch some sleep...just in case."

"Just in case you could pronounce him before you went to bed?"

Peter shifted in his spot. Why did his words sometimes sound so stupid? "Well, I'm not actually going to get any sleep tonight," he blurted out. For a moment he considered telling Irene the real truth—that if Mr. Harris did die tonight, he didn't know if he could stand it. He had too many things to deal with and he didn't feel able to control any of them: pneumonia, death, internship.

"Here," Irene said. "Put this in the drawer, would you?" She tossed Peter a small white bottle and, bending over the patient, began to massage his back, kneading and smoothing his bare skin, which had, Peter noticed, turned the color of Silly Putty.

Why does she even bother, he wondered. Why doesn't she just sit down in the chair next to the bed and read or doze, as he'd seen some of the night nurses do?

"Peripheral circulation closes down when patients are near death," Irene said, as if reading his mind. "The skin gets clammy and that makes them feel cold. Massage helps. Even if it doesn't, it lets Mr. Harris know I'm here."

She finished the back rub and guided Mr. Harris down flat again, balancing the slight weight of him and settling him gently. "There you go, Jim," she said. Irene smoothed a wisp of his hair back into place.

Peter's feet were aching. Even his most comfortable sneakers felt like vises after twenty hours. The plastic-covered visitor's chair at the bedside looked tempting. He turned his gaze back to the patient, trying to think of something clinical to say. "His breathing seems easier. More regular."

"Thank you for increasing the morphine," Irene said. She pulled up the bed rails, and they snapped into place with an authoritative click.

"You're welcome," said Peter.

"If we were in Mr. Harris's home," Irene said, "I'd open a window."

Peter flopped down in the chair and hooked his heels onto the bottom rung of the bed rail. Immediately the pressure on his toes eased.

"When my grandfather was dying," Peter said, before he even knew what he was thinking, "my mother opened his bedroom windows. It was May, and the air smelled like my grandmother's garden." He swiveled his feet on the rail. "I can still remember the smell of peat moss and gardenias."

"How old was he?"

"About eighty-four, I think. Same age as Mr. Harris here."

"Mr. Harris owned a series of grocery stores," Irene said. "He started with one little mom and pop store about the size of this room. By the time he turned the business over to his son-in-law, he had a chain of supermarkets all over the northeast. His wife died four years ago of a brain tumor."

"How do you know all that?" Peter asked.

"One of his daughters told me. It was hard for him to give up the business, but he felt he was getting too old to compete."

"Scary to get old," Peter said.

"It's certainly not for the faint of heart," Irene said with a sad smile. "What did your grandfather do?"

"He was a tailor. I used to hang out in his shop while he fitted customers or made suits. He'd hang the measuring tape around my neck and I'd be in charge of the pins. He'd be sewing with his machine, come to a pin and, without stopping, take it out and hand it to me to stick into the pincushion. It was our ritual. Then he'd take me out for ice cream."

"You said you didn't remember much about him."

"I don't really, not much. I remember the night he died."

"You were there?"

Peter nodded. He was vaguely aware that the circulation had returned to his feet. "After dinner my mother told me to go in to say good-bye to him—she thought it wouldn't be long. Then she made me go upstairs to bed. I couldn't sleep. I kept hearing him make these choking noises. When he died, I could hear everyone crying. I stayed in my bed and stared at the ceiling, imagining what awful things were going on downstairs. I tried to cry too, but I couldn't. To me, he wasn't dead, he was still my grandfather sewing in his shop and buying me ice cream."

"Have you ever seen anyone die?" Irene asked.

Peter put his elbows on his knees and ran his hands through his hair. It felt greasy, uncombed. His belly still burned and grumbled. "Not really. I saw one guy who didn't survive a code, but that wasn't like a natural death."

"It's funny," Irene said. "I gave a talk about death and dying once, and when I asked people to raise their hands if they'd ever been with someone at the moment of death, the exact moment that death occurred, almost all the nurses and nurses' aides raised their hands. Not many doctors did."

Irene walked around the bed, stepping over Peter's feet. She lifted the sheet from Mr. Harris's legs, slipped in a bed cradle, then settled the sheets over the cradle. "His feet and legs seem more sensitive to pressure now," she said, sitting in the chair next to Peter's and moving it closer to the bed. She took Mr. Harris's hand and put her other hand a little higher up on his arm. "Jim?" she said. "Are you more comfortable now? I'm here with you."

Peter watched her. She looked tired before, and now she looked as exhausted as Peter felt.

"Judging by his breathing and his skin color," she said, "we're going to get really busy in a couple of hours." Irene turned to him with a look on her face that was almost sly. "If you're up to it."

At 4:35 a.m., Peter returned. Classical music was playing on the radio, and the lights were dim. Irene was reading something to Mr. Harris.

"You still up, Peter?" She didn't seem surprised to see him.

"Actually, I got to lie down for a few minutes. The woman with the fever stabilized." Yawning, he plopped down in the chair. Its plastic cushion deflated under him with a hiss of air. "I can't sleep when I'm on call anyway. I keep waiting for the beeper to go off. What are you reading to Mr. Harris?"

"A letter from his daughter. She writes every day, something about their lives, her memories of her childhood."

"You seem pretty close to the family."

"I suppose I've become a connection to their father, but I don't know that I'm really close to them. The older I get," Irene said, "the more I find myself pulling back from getting too involved." She shook her head. "Maybe it's time to go on vacation."

"Strange how patients move in and out of our lives, isn't it?" Peter asked, although he had not yet been really close to any of his patients.

Mr. Harris's irregular breathing filled the silence. Then Irene said, "I don't know. I find that I remember them. Your grandfather—he was your mother's father?"

"Yup. Poppy, we called him."

Raising her voice, Irene said, "Jim, your doctor, Peter, is here with us again. He called *his* grandfather Poppy." She looked at Peter as if to say, your turn.

Peter cleared his throat. "Hello, Mr. Harris," he said. "I've been working with your internist for the last few weeks. I admitted you to the hospital." He looked at Irene for some signal that he had said the right thing. She stroked Mr. Harris's hand.

"You're doing great, Jim," she said. "Don't worry. We're here with you."

Peter stood up and walked to the small corkboard where Mr. Harris's daughter had pinned family photographs. There was a photo of Mr. Harris as a young man, gaunt and serious, with a white grocery apron around his waist. In another, he had his arm around a stunning young woman, tiny and small boned. The other photos showed Mr. Harris and his wife with one or both of their daughters, a series in which each of them aged until Mr. Harris was an old man, holding grandchildren on his hip or cradling them in his arms. His wife was gray and fading, then absent, and his daughters became women, their faces a reflection of their parents.

Peter tapped one of the pictures. "It's too bad we never really know who our patients are. They come in sick or out of it, like Mr. Harris here, at the end of their lives." He sat down again, pulling his chair a little closer to the bed rails. "I don't know if it helps or hurts to see them as whole people. It makes all this even harder."

He reached through the bed rails to squeeze Mr. Harris's arm. "What a great family you have," he said. "Your wife was beautiful."

He sat there in the dim light with Irene and Mr. Harris. Between the back and forth sawing of Mr. Harris's breathing, Peter heard the loud ticking of the wall clock. Through the hospital window, a faint glow rose from the parking lot. In the hallway, the night nurses walked back and forth on squishy soles, whispering.

"Do you have any kids?" Peter asked.

"I have three boys and one girl. All of them grown up, three engaged. I'm preparing to look in the mirror one day and see a grandmother staring back at me." She paused. "What about you?"

Peter shrugged. "Not a whole lot of time for social life these days." He nodded toward Mr. Harris. "How are his vital signs?"

"I've stopped taking them," Irene said. "Help me pull him up again, would you?"

They bent together over Mr. Harris, hooked their arms under his, and slid him higher in the bed.

"He's got a lot of hair for an old guy," Peter said. "My grandfather was totally bald, except for a mustache."

"It's funny," Irene said. "But after a while, all my patients remind me of someone in my family."

"Really?" said Peter.

"Or maybe I pretend that they do." She stood by the window for a moment. "All the young women seem like my mother. She died from ovarian cancer when she was thirty-nine. And all the old ones remind me of my grandparents. Or my father, who's getting old now too."

Peter's heart started pounding. He noticed this clinically, as if he were his own physician. He'd never talked about death before, not like this. Talking about death openly made him feel odd, but oddly alive.

At 6:15 a.m., after he'd been to 3-East to see about a post-op lady who'd pulled out her IV and to 7-South to write a Percocet order, Peter returned again to room 23B.

A deep fuchsia seeped through the window. The bed rail was down and Irene was sitting on the bed next to Mr. Harris, who was propped almost upright on his pillows. She held his hand and chanted "ahhh" along with each of his exhalations. Peter listened from the doorway. It sounded to him as if they were singing together, or praying.

Irene didn't seem to notice Peter entering. And Peter—seeing Mr. Harris's eyes open, rolled back in his head, and the nurse, leaning in close toward her patient—stopped several yards short of the bed. Mr. Harris's breathing was harsh and deep as he fought to pull each breath into the depths of his frail body. With each shudder, Irene leaned farther forward. As each breath squeezed out of the patient's lungs with a prolonged groan, Irene joined in, her *ah* a controlled, musical harmony. When Mr. Harris's breathing slowed, Irene followed his lead. Peter stepped closer.

"You're just in time," Irene said, motioning for him to sit on the other side of the bed. "I called his daughter, but I don't think she'll make it. He doesn't seem to want to wait."

Peter put down the bed rail and sat next to the patient, whose body was barely a sunken disturbance in the sheets. "Put your hand on his arm," Irene said. "Let him know you're here." Then, more loudly, "Peter and I are here with you, Jim. I'll take care of Carly when she gets here. Everything will be all right."

Mr. Harris stared up at the ceiling, his eyes filmed over and dull, his mouth opening, then falling shut with every breath.

"Are you okay?" Peter asked.

"Not really," Irene said without looking away from Mr. Harris. "Are you?"

They heard a commotion in another room. Someone dropped something metallic that clanged and bounced. Voices rose and fell. An aide came into the room with a breakfast tray and Irene waved her away.

"What was that sound you were making?" Peter asked.

"It's called breathing with a patient," Irene said. "It's like going part of the way with them, a way of letting your life and their death overlap." She glanced at him. " Do you want to try?"

Peter didn't know what to say.

"It's easy. You don't have to do anything," she said. "Watch Jim's chest rise and fall and just breathe along with him."

In the hall, the day shift nurses were arriving. Peter could smell coffee brewing. The voices of residents, debating some lab value, moved close to the door and then down the hall. Mr. Harris sucked in another deep breath, then— with a harsh, terrible groan—let it out. Irene joined in with her *ah*, sustaining her note, then letting it fade away with Mr. Harris's breath. Peter leaned closer; before he thought about it, his lips parted as he offered his own *ah*, a whisper that was as involuntary as one person's yawn in response to another's.

"Good," Irene said to Peter. Then to the patient she said, "It's okay, Jim. We're both here with you."

She held her arm fast around Mr. Harris's shoulders, her hair frizzy in the morning light.

"This is it," she whispered, and Peter felt a sudden grip of anxiety. But as Mr. Harris let go a final, slow moan of air, Peter found himself joining in, his deeper *ah* blending with Mr. Harris's and Irene's, the three notes braiding around one another. Mr. Harris's lips paled, his eyes darkened, and together their three breaths rose into the room, fading out in unison. ❧

Whatever is Left

Cortney Davis

My patient miscarried
this week in the ER.
A nurse took the 16-week
conceptus, slipped it
into a cup, hurried
it away. Today,
the woman asks if she
can have it back—
Lo que quede, she says,
Whatever is left.

Permits must be signed.
Come back tomorrow.

Now, it's tomorrow;
I hand her a plastic cup
wrapped and taped so
no one can see
what's inside. She presses it
to her belly. *Boy,* she asks, *or girl?*
If I open the cup, what will I see?

Boy, I say.
Blood and small bones.

I walk her to the elevator.
She says, *Thank you.*
Marco, she adds, raising
the cup. *My son's name.*

❧

Postoperative Care

Arlene Eager

Glad to be alive,
I look in mirrors
with detachment.
I study my seams.
My belly looks like
a garment taken in
by a tailor's apprentice,
the crazy one
he had to fire.

&

Contributors' Notes

Dannie Abse is a Welsh-born physician and poet. His most recent books to appear in the U.S.A. are his novel, *The Strange Case of Dr. Simmonds and Dr. Glas* (2002, short-listed for the Booker Prize), and a collection of his later poems, *The Yellow Bird* (2004). His book *The Two Roads Taken* (2003) describes how he pursued the vocations of Medicine and Literature. Dr. Abse is a Fellow of the Royal Society of Literature and President of the Welsh Academy.

Kelli Russell Agodon is the author of *Small Knots* (Cherry Grove Collections) and *Geography*, winner of the 2003 Floating Bridge Press Chapbook Award. Her poems have appeared in numerous journals and on NPR's "The Writer's Almanac" with Garrison Keillor. She's the recipient of two Washington State Artist Trust grants, the James Hearst Poetry Prize, and the Carlin Aden Award for formal verse. www.agodon.com

Jacob M. Appel received an M.F.A. in fiction from New York University and a J.D. from Harvard Law School. His short fiction has recently appeared in *Agni, StoryQuarterly* and *Southwest Review*. Jacob teaches medical ethics at Brown University and writing at the Gotham Writers Workshop.

Priscilla Atkins lives in Holland, Michigan. Her poems have appeared in *Epoch*, *Southern Humanities Review*, *The Southern Review*, *The Bellingham Review*, *Smartish Pace*, and an earlier issue of *Bellevue Literary Review*.

Melisa (Misha) Cahnmann is an Assistant Professor in the Department of Language and Literacy Education at the University of Georgia. She has published poems in *APR, Quarterly West, Barrow Street, River City, Laurel Review,* and *Red Rock Review*. She is currently pursuing an MFA at New England College. The Dorothy Sargent Rosenberg Foundation awarded her top prize for poems reflecting "the spirit of life."

Rafael Campo teaches and practices internal medicine at Harvard Medical School. His recent books include *Diva*, a finalist for the National Book Critics Circle Award in poetry; *Landscape with Human Figure*, winner of the Gold Medal from *ForeWord* for the best book of poetry published by an independent press; and *The Healing Art: A Doctor's Black Bag of Poetry*, essays on poetry and healing. New poems, essays, and reviews have appeared or are forthcoming in *The Boston Review, Commonweal, The Georgia Review, The Nation, Prairie Schooner, The Progressive,* and *River Styx*. www.rafaelcampo.com

Katie Chaple's poems have appeared in *32 Poems, The Antioch Review, The Southern Poetry Review,* and *Rattle.* She currently works as an assistant editor on *Five Points* and as the managing editor of *Terminus.*

Cortney Davis, a nurse practitioner, is the author of *Leopold's Maneuvers,* winner of the 2003 Prairie Schooner Book Prize in Poetry. *I Knew a Woman,* a memoir about her work in women's health, was published by Random House in 2001 and won the Connecticut Center for the Book Non-Fiction Award. Her other poetry collections are *The Body Flute* and *Details of Flesh.* www.cortneydavis.com

Matthew Davis is a second-year graduate student at the University of Iowa's Nonfiction Writing Program. His writings about Mongolia have appeared in several magazines, most recently in the Fall 2004 issue of *WorldView Magazine.* He is an Iowa Arts Tuition Scholarship recipient and a Stanley Fellow. Currently, he is at work on a book about Mongolia.

Sariah Dorbin received an MFA from the Bennington Writing Seminars. Her fiction has appeared in *The Antioch Review.* She lives in Los Angeles, where she is currently at work on a novel.

Erika Dreifus's fiction has appeared or is forthcoming in *Lilith, MississippiReview.com, Solander: The Magazine of the Historical Novel Society, Southern Indiana Review,* and *Vermont Literary Review.* Her writing honors include first prize in the David Dornstein Memorial Creative Writing Contest, a Prague Summer Program scholarship, and residencies at the Vermont Studio Center and the Kimmel Harding Nelson Center for the Arts. An active freelance writer and teacher, Erika also publishes a free monthly newsletter, "The Practicing Writer." www.practicing-writer.com

Arlene Eager's poems have appeared in *The Hudson Review, Five Points, Atlanta Review, The Southern Review,* and the anthology *Essential Love.* She leads workshops in the study, discussion and writing of poetry in Stony Brook, Long Island. She and her husband Bill split their time between New York and Maine.

Marcia Calhoun Forecki's first book, *Speak to Me,* which described the discovery of her son's deafness, won a Book Award from the President's Committee on Employment of the Handicapped. She has written short stories, articles, and a screenplay, and is currently at work on a novel. Forecki teaches English as a Second Language and Spanish at Iowa Western Community College. Her parents are from rural communities in southern Missouri and Kentucky, places that have formed Eulalia in her writing.

Vishwas R. Gaitonde received a medical degree from the University of Madras, India and an MA in journalism from the University of Iowa. His book, *A Thief in the Night: Understanding AIDS,* was published in 2001 by East-West Books, Chennai (Madras). His articles, essays, and fiction have appeared in India, Great Britain, and the US. He enjoys acting in the amateur theatre, and has appeared in three television plays in India. He runs Quill & Pill, a medical writing company in La Jolla, California, and has just completed a novel.

Andrea Lewis writes short fiction at her home on Vashon Island, Washington. She is a founding member of Richard Hugo House, a popular literary arts center in Seattle. Her thirty-year writing career began with technical writing in the microcomputer software industry. Andrea was raised in Albuquerque, New Mexico, and her fiction has appeared in *New Mexico Humanities Review.*

Karin Lin-Greenberg's fiction has appeared in or is forthcoming in *Eclipse, Karamu,* and *Redivider.* In 2004, she won the *Pittsburgh City Paper's* fiction contest. She is currently at the University of Pittsburgh where she is teaching and pursuing an MFA in fiction.

Lou Lipsitz is a psychotherapist and poet living in Chapel Hill, NC. He has published three books of poems, the latest of which, *Seeking the Hook,* can be obtained at www.loulipsitz.com. His psychotherapy work includes a special focus on men's issues and midlife transitions.

Evan Lyon is a resident in internal medicine at Brigham and Women's Hospital in Boston. He divides his clinical time equally between rural Haiti and the U.S. In Haiti, he works with Partners In Health—a community-based non-profit organization that provides comprehensive medical care to the poor of Haiti's Central Plateau.

Susan Bloom Malus lives in Brooklyn and Red Rock, NY. In 2005, she won the Briar Cliff Review's creative nonfiction competition, and was a semi-finalist for both the Writers-at-Work Creative Non-Fiction Competition and Portfolio's Dana Award. Her fiction has appeared in *NDQ, Coming Out,* and *Junction magazine.* She has an MFA in fiction from Brooklyn College where she received the Mintz Memorial Award for writing excellence.

Shannon McNamara received an MFA from Sarah Lawrence College. She was the recipient of the Collected Works Bookstore Scholarship to participate in the Santa Fe Writers' Conference in 2004. Her fiction has recently appeared in

Cimarron Review and is forthcoming in *Confrontation*. She lives in Santa Fe, New Mexico.

Carolyn Megan's work has appeared in *The Massachusetts Review*, *The Kenyon Review*, *South Dakota Review* and *MS. Magazine*. She lives in Maine.

Joan Michelson lives in Britain and teaches creative writing at Birkbeck College, the University of London. Her chapbook, *Letting in the Light,* was Editor's Choice publication in a PoeticMatrix competition. She has published fiction and poems in both Britain and the United States. Her poem "Amen" won first prize in the 2005 Londonart International judged by poet laureate of England, Andrew Motion. She directs the UK poetry performance venue 'Sounding the American Voice.'

Susan Moger has published short fiction on *The New York Times* Op-Ed Page, and studied fiction writing with Marguerite Young, Robert Stone, Barbara Kingsolver, and Larry Heinemann. Her book, *Teaching the Diary of Anne Frank* (Scholastic Professional Books) won an Ed Press award in 1999. She is finishing her first novel and teaching in the Writing Program at Anne Arundel (Maryland) Community College.

Robert Oldshue is a primary care physician in Boston and received an MFA in creative writing from Warren Wilson College. His fiction has appeared twice previously in *Bellevue Literary Review*. His essay, "Code Blue," is forthcoming in *The Gettysburg Review*.

William Orem's first collection of stories, *Zombi, You My Love*, won the GLCA New Writers Award for 2000. His poetry and short fiction have appeared in over 45 publications and have twice been nominated for the Pushcart Prize. He works in Boston as an editor and science writer, and is currently seeking representation.

Leslie Patterson is working on a book of short stories about the Impressionist artists, Manet, Degas, and Morisot. Another part in this series was published in spring 2005 in *Ballyhoo Stories*.

Simon Perchik is an attorney whose poems have appeared in *Partisan Review, Bellevue Literary Review, The New Yorker,* and elsewhere. Readers who would like to learn more about him are invited to read "Magic, Illusion and Other Realities" at www.geocities.com/simonthepoet, which lists a complete bibliography.

Holly Posner, author of *Explorations in American Culture*, has taught at the New School, Hunter College, and New York University. She received an MFA from Sarah Lawrence, where she was the editor of the graduate literary journal. Currently, she is a mentor for the Hadar Foundation, which sponsors scholarships in the creative arts. She is the winner of the 2005 Greenburgh Poetry Competition; her work has appeared or is forthcoming in *Lumina*, *Rattapallax*, and *The Laurel Review*.

Sharon Pretti lives in San Francisco. Her work has appeared in *The Healing Muse*, *Santa Clara Review*, *Sonoma Mandala Literary Review*, and is forthcoming in *Marin Poetry Center Anthology* and *Margie: The American Journal of Poetry*. In addition to her practice as a medical social worker, she runs Age of Expression, which provides poetry writing workshops to senior citizens in long-term care and residential facilities.

Eve Rifkah is the co-founder and artistic director of Poetry Oasis, Inc., a non-profit poetry organization, and editor of *Diner: a journal of poetry*. Poems and essays have appeared in *The MacGuffin*, *5 AM*, *Chaffin Journal*, *Porcupine Press*, *The Worcester Review*, *California Quarterly*, *ReDactions*, *Jabberwock Review*, *Southern New Hampshire Literary Journal* and have been translated into Braille. Her chapbook *At the Leprosarium* won the 2003 Revelever chapbook contest. She received an MFA in Writing from Vermont College and lives with her husband, poet Michael Milligan.

Margaret A. Robinson has published novels, short stories, and poems. Her chapbook, *Sparks*, is available at Pudding House Publications. Robinson teaches in the Writing Center and Creative Writing Program at Widener University, and lives in Swarthmore, PA.

Laurie Rosenblatt teaches at Harvard Medical School and practices psychiatry at Dana-Farber Cancer Institute and Brigham & Women's Hospital. In addition to medical publications, she has published poems in *JAMA*, *Medical Humanities*, *Borderlands: Texas Poetry Review*, and *Academic Medicine*. "Toledo, Ohio: 1967" is the first poem in a longer work entitled, "Arcas Inverse: A Biography," which was inspired by her brother Tom's life and death with AIDS.

Katherine Soniat's *The Fire Setters* is available through Web Del Sol Online Chapbook Series. Her fourth collection, *Alluvial*, was published by Bucknell University Press, and *A Shared Life* won the Iowa Poetry Prize. Poems are in recent issues of the *Iowa Review, Virginia Quarterly, New Letters, Quarterly West,* and *Hotel Amerika.* She lives in Blacksburg, Virginia and teaches in the MFA Program at Virginia Tech.

Peter Sordillo has advanced degrees in medicine, philosophy and physics, and has published more than 130 scientific papers in cancer research and biophysics. He is an attending medical oncologist at Lenox Hill Hospital, and lives in New York City with his wife and three children. His poetry has most recently appeared in *The Iowa Review*

John Stone's latest book is *Music From Apartment 8: New and Selected Poems* (Louisiana State University Press, 2004). He co-edits *On Doctoring,* the anthology presented by the Robert Wood Johnson Foundation to all U.S. medical students since 1990. Stone is Professor of Medicine, Emeritus, at Emory University, where he has often taught in the English Department.

Pat Tompkins is an editor in the San Francisco Bay Area. Her essays, reviews, stories, and poems have appeared in the *Writer, Copperfield Review, Threads, Paumanok Review,* and the *San Francisco Chronicle.* She first heard about Carville when she moved to Louisiana at age seven.

Katya Uroff lives in Longmeadow, Massachusetts. Her short fiction has appeared in *The Worcester Review, Green Hills Literary Lantern, Primavera, Carve Magazine, pindeldyboz, The Timber Creek Review,* and *Words of Wisdom.*

Glenn Vanstrum is a practicing anesthesiologist. His book, *The Saltwater Wilderness* (Oxford University Press, 2003), won the San Diego Book Award in Science, Nature, and Technology. He has published non-fiction essays in *Sierra, California Wild,* and the *Los Angeles Times.* "The Hangover" was adapted from his novel, *Let Fall Thy Blade.*

Susan Varon is a poet and artist living in New York City. She began writing poetry in 1992, after suffering a severe stroke. Her work has appeared in over 30 publications, including *Green Mountains Review, The Midwestern Quarterly* and *Notre Dame Review.* In 1999 she won the New Voice Poetry Award of the Writer's Voice, and was awarded a residency at The MacDowell Colony. She has since been granted fellowships at Hedgebrook, The Blue Mountain Center, and the Helene Wurlitzer Foundation. She was ordained an Interfaith Minister in June, 2005.

Acknowledgements

The *Bellevue Literary Review* would like to express its deep gratitude to all who have helped support the journal in its efforts to bridge the worlds of literature and medicine.

Founder: The Vilcek Foundation

Scribe: The Lucius N. Littauer Foundation

Publishers: Dr. Alec S. Goldenberg, Lenox Hill Hospital

Benefactors: Anonymous, Drs. Anthony & Elayne Mustalish, Pfizer Inc.

Muses: H. Dale & Elizabeth Hemmerdinger, Lola Finkelstein, Rita J. & Stanley H. Kaplan Family Foundation, Dr. Katherine Mathews, Lynne Mijangos, Dr. Franco Muggia, Eleanor Jackson Piel, Mieko Willoughby

Friends: Dr. Edward L. Amorosi, Dr. Frances Bailen-Rose, Dr. Michael S. Bruno, Dr. Ralph Crawshaw, Maggie Jacobs, Dr. Martin L. Kahn, Dr. Sandra Kammerman, Dr. Robert Maslansky, Dr. & Mrs. Rodney Ulane

Supporters: Dr. Tracy Breen, Dr. Max E. Cytryn, Gail Dearden, Dr. Charles H. Debrovner, Dr. Arthur Charles Fox, Dr. Joan Cusack Handler, Dr. Charles S. Hirsch, Bernice L. Lewis, Dr. Robin Lifton, Dr. Arthur E. Lindner, Dr. Mark S. Lipton, Dr. Sander H. Mendelson, Dr. Andrew Milano, Dr. Diana Nilsen, Dr. Lionel A. Rudolph, Susan Scheid, Dr. Emilia Sedlis, Dr. Rhonda L. Soricelli, Dr. Norton Spritz, Gilbert Tauber

----

We welcome your support as we continue to explore the connections between literature and medicine. All patrons will be recognized in the journal.

$75 (Supporter), $150 (Friend), and $250 (Muse) -- *each includes one-year subscription for you and a friend*
$500 (Benefactor) and $1000 (Publisher) -- *each includes three-year subscription for you and a friend*
$5000 (Scribe) and $10,000 (Founder) -- *each includes life-time subscription*

The *Bellevue Literary Review* is part of NYU School of Medicine, a 501(c)(3) charitable organization. All contributions are tax-deductible. Please make checks payable to *Bellevue Literary Review*.

Bellevue Literary Review, Department of Medicine, NYU School of Medicine
550 First Avenue, OBV-A612, New York, NY 10016
www.BLReview.org